Where the Great River Bends

A natural and human history of the Columbia at Wallula

Robert J. Carson, Michael E. Denny, Catherine E. Dickson, Lawrence L. Dodd and G. Thomas Edwards

Edited by Robert J. Carson

With a foreword by Donald Snow

KEOKEE BOOKS

Sandpoint, Idaho

Whitman College, Walla Walla, Washington 99362

Published with grants from Fort Walla Walla Museum and the National Natural Landmarks program of the National Park Service

Second printing 2011

Printed in the United States of America

Photographs by Robert Baker, Robert J. Carson, John Clement, Paul Clement, Michael E. Denny, Kathryn Farrell Guizar, Dianne Kornberg and others

Cover photos: *Wallula Gap Twilight* (front) and *Wallula Moonrise* and *Juniper at Wallula Gap* (back) by John Clement; historic photos courtesy Whitman College and Northwest Archives and Virgil Reynolds Collection

Published by Keokee Books, an imprint of Keokee Co. Publishing, Inc.
P.O. Box 722
Sandpoint, ID 83864
208-263-3573
www.KeokeeBooks.com

Publisher's Cataloging-in-Publication Data
Where the great river bends : a natural and human history of the Columbia at Wallula / by Robert J. Carson ... [et al.] ; edited by Robert J.
    Carson with a foreword by Donald Snow.
        Includes bibliographic references.
        Includes index.
        1. Columbia River Basin–Geography. 2. Columbia River Basin–Natural history. 3. Columbia River Basin–Geology. 4. Columbia
River Basin–History. 5. Wallula (Washington)–History, local. I. Title. II. Carson, Robert J.
979.7
ISBN 978-1-879628-32-8an

" 'Wallula' is in the Walla Walla language and means the same as 'Walla Walla' in the Nez Perce language. So to Native Americans, 'Wallula' means 'small rapid river,' 'running water,' 'ripple after ripple' or 'fall after fall.' Another meaning is 'a small stream running into a larger one,' that is, where the Walla Walla River joins the Columbia River."

–Edmond S. Meany, 1923, *Origin of Washington Geographic Names*

Contents

Foreword

The first time I saw Wallula Gap, I saw it in the way most people do nowadays – through the windows of a speeding automobile. I admit that I have only a fuzzy recollection of that moment – or series of moments – when I first beheld the remarkable notch, a vast absence in a vast ridgeline, where the Columbia River, called *Nč'i wana* in the Sahaptin language of Mid-Columbia Plateau tribes, makes its dramatic and final bend to the west. I was a new resident of eastern Washington then, having recently arrived for a teaching job in Walla Walla, but even as a newcomer, I could sense the significance of the gap.

Many years earlier, while living in Missoula, Montana, I accidentally ran across a book titled *Cataclysms on the Columbia*, a fascinating account of the geologist J Harlen Bretz and his iconoclastic theories about the mammoth Ice Age floods that had shaped the face of eastern Washington. First writing in the 1920s, Bretz had been a catastrophist within a field dominated by uniformitarian theories of geology. His flood theory struck many of his geological brethren as Biblical diluvian nonsense, but Bretz persisted, and the evidence mounted. Ultimately, the idea of repeated ice-dam floods originating from Glacial Lake Missoula achieved acceptance.

As I drove along U.S. Highway 12 for the first time, nearing Wallula Gap, I remember letting out a little gasp. Here, at last, I thought: *the Missoula-Wallula connection!* Mine was the sort of visceral reaction a nonscientist often experiences when a rather dry scientific concept, encountered only in the abstract, leaps from the pages of a book and lands with the force of a story, or a picture.

Looking at the gap, I could suddenly *see* what Bretz had been talking about. A wall of icy water, traveling about as fast as my Buick, had encountered this narrowest-possible neck at the bottom of the 20,000-square-mile jug we now call the Mid-Columbia Basin. The water could not exit through the gap quickly enough to keep pace with the super-fast flow that had drained Glacial Lake Missoula hundreds of miles away, a body of water about the size of Lake Erie. Wallula Gap had formed a temporary hydraulic dam, partially stoppering the largest floods the planet has ever seen and causing a massive backup, until the suddenly formed, ice-cold reservoir – we now call it Lake Lewis – had in places overtopped the thousand-foot-high Horse Heaven Hills. Something like this had happened not once but dozens of times, over thousands of years. After the waters

Old postcard (Ellis 2864) titled "Looking North Through 'The Gap' Wallula Cut Off." (Robert A. Bennett Collection)

receded, crashing through the Columbia Gorge at interstate highway speeds, the Mid-Columbia Basin lay changed.

What had been mildly undulating prairie was now, over vast areas, scoured down to bedrock – the Channeled Scabland. Places where the waters slowed and backed up in huge eddies, dropping mind-numbing quantities of silt, were now massive pillows of lush soil – the Touchet Beds. And here and there, across much of the Mid-Columbia Basin, the floodwaters had deposited huge chunks of granite that had hitched a ride atop icebergs carried from northern Idaho. These rocks – granitic erratics, as geologists call them – were the first clues that had led J Harlen Bretz to his earth-rattling theory of catastrophic floods. Bretz had helped revise his field, much as the floods he described had revised the face of eastern Washington.

The West is so full of dramatic landscapes and massive vistas that we who live here often take them for granted. Traveling as we do, most of the time by motorcar, we tend to encounter the very wonders of the world as a highly generalized landscape, a blur of geography, geology, biota and cultural artifact. Perhaps we forget what the combination of velocity and comfort does to our perceptions. Inside the climate-controlled chamber of a Toyota or a Buick, it's easy to overlook the fact that *landscape* is as much an event as it is a portrait. The speed of the car works a bit like the shutter of a camera, giving us a sort of snapshot of a given place, but that "picture," even if we continue to hold it in memory, tends to mask more than it reveals.

As the book you are now holding in your hands surely attests, places like Wallula Gap help us to expand our sense of space and time, and the chapters herein can really enhance the imagination, for these five writers reveal dimensions of the place that simply cannot be seen through the windows of a speeding automobile.

Think of the difference it would make if we were to approach Wallula Gap not on the plush cushions of a Detroit Barcalounger doing 65, but rather on foot or horseback, as thousands of westward travelers did on their way to the lush valleys of coastal Oregon Territory. Or from the hard seats of a wooden canoe, a trim but heavy boat made in the old Nez Perce way, as Lewis and Clark learned, by carefully burning the heart out of the trunk of a fat yellow pine. Think of what you would see, smell, hear, fear, even taste if you approached the gap at pedestrian speed, the approximate speed of the river itself, undammed. Nothing would flash past your eyes, bypass your nose, or fail to land upon your ears. Nothing would devolve into the two-dimensional motion picture we perceive as "landscape" through the shatterproof glass of a hurtling automobile.

Let's run our first trip to Wallula Gap again but this time in slow motion, pedestrian motion.

Approaching the gap from the Washington side, you would see along the Horse Heaven Hills mechanical proof of the most notable and noted meteorological feature of the place: wind. More than 450 electrical turbines stand along that eolian spine, where wind velocities average 16 mph to 18 mph year-round. The three adjacent wind farms here – Stateline, Vansycle and Combine Hills – constitute the largest wind-electrical site on the planet and make a bold nod to the angels of alternative energy. Yet, the wind is also a demon at Wallula Gap. As G. Thomas Edwards' chapter on 19th century history in this book informs us, people have always cursed the Wallula wind. It blows grit into one's pancakes, hurts the eyes of livestock, forms massive dunes in the little canyons that feed into the gap. That someone might be ingenious enough to profit from today's

View north along the Columbia River through Wallula Gap to the Pasco Basin. (Bob Baker photo)

Wallula Gap wind is a fact that would have astonished the residents of yore. Pay attention to Lawrence L. Dodd's chapter on the evolving economies of the Wallula Gap region in the 20th century, and you'll get a sense of how tenuous and difficult the matter of making a living here has always been.

Slow down even more. Take out your binoculars and watch the birds. Depending on the season, you're likely to see an astonishing assembly of waterbirds. Whimbrels and wigeons, long-billed curlews, western sandpipers, greater and lesser yellowlegs, white pelicans – these and many other species can be found cruising the wave tops and edges of *Nč'i wana,* while several species of swifts and swallows, rock wrens, falcons, and great soaring hawks populate the cliffs, walls and banks of the gap. All of this and more are nicely documented in Mike Denny's chapter on biology herein, "Seasons in the Sun." Besides birds, I have seen bighorn sheep, mule deer and badgers (well, one badger) in the Juniper Canyon section of the gap. The Wallula area – the gap itself, the side canyons and wetlands where the Walla Walla River empties into the Columbia – represents one portion of eastern Washington where wildlife remains abundant enough to ease my pining for Montana, my home for 25 years.

Stop and think about the prehistoric human occupation of the area over the slow march of time – not the 200 years that Euro-Americans have inhabited this region of stark cliffs and silty soils, but the thousands of years of occupancy and use that preceded our quaint idea of "settlement." The name "Wallula" apparently derives from "Walúulapam," one of the Native American bands who lived in

View south through Wallula Gap from the rail yard at Wallula. (Bob Carson photo)

Dawn at Wallula Gap is captured in this Arnold Studio photograph that was hand colored by Mrs. Arnold. (Fred A. Mitchell Collection)

the fertile valley of the Walla Walla River. It is not known how long human beings have occupied the harsh and difficult landscapes of the Mid-Columbia, in part because the floods that occurred around the end of the Pleistocene – 15,000 years ago – wiped out the evidence archaeologists use to identify material culture. As Catherine Dickson carefully documents here, the several tribes who best knew the Wallula Gap were at first seminomadic people who were clever and strong enough to kill the now-extinct woolly mammoth and remained dependent on the rich runs of Columbia River salmon long after the mammoth was gone.

Wallula Gap is a place where our sense of time can feel as palpable, as ambient, as the air and water that course through the canyon. Bob Carson's chapter on geology, "Fire and Flood along the Columbia," will bend your mind with astonishing images of time, scale and the very plasticity of the earth. Think of flood basalts burbling up from gigantic fissures in the planet's crust. Think of the resulting rock as frozen magma, miles deep. Think of volcanic ejecta from Cascade volcanoes falling in blizzards of superfine ash over thousands of square miles. Think of a dramatic landscape in southeastern Washington composed in no small part of materials delivered by water from Montana.

The river through the gap is a river no more; it is a reservoir now, as is most of the entire Columbia. The foaming rapids and dancing riffles are gone, and the thought of Columbia River floods is now a mere chimera of imagination. Yet the vibrancy and vividness of the place remain, obdurate as basalt. You can feel it in the wind, smell it in the rock and sand, almost hear it in the faint echoes of time. With the help of these five authors, you can see Wallula Gap in multiple dimensions, similar to how I first beheld this impressive

slot in the rock and was able finally to see what J Harlen Bretz had taught. It's a desert place – shocking to some, inspiring to others – and it is a place worth knowing. Do your homework; go see it; let your imagination do the rest.

–Don Snow
Senior Lecturer of Environmental Studies, Whitman College

Preface

Like Meriwether Lewis and William Clark, I came from Virginia to the Pacific Northwest. Imagine how we felt to first behold the mighty Columbia River, so much bigger than Virginia's James River. My first trip to Wallula Gap was with Bill Reeve, a student at Whitman College. I had given up tenure at an eastern university to become the lone geology professor at this liberal arts college. I was quite impressed with the cliffs rising 800 feet above the reservoir at Wallula Gap, where Bill showed me some of the lava flows studied by his previous professor, Dick Clem, who had died the year before. Professor Clem had also studied the large mammals that became extinct about 10,000 years ago, whose bones are found here and there in the flood and wind deposits of southeastern Washington. As you will learn, the constricted nature of Wallula Gap is responsible for a lot of the deposits of the Earth's greatest-known floods.

Soon I learned that Wallula Gap offers more than geology and scenery.

The reservoir is good for fishing and sailing; the Twin Sisters (Two Sisters), famous in Native American legend, have short but challenging rock climbs; and the hiking is fascinating because of a diverse landscape with varied geology and wildlife. The higher one hikes, the better the view. Back in 2002, I decided to write a book on the geography and geology of Wallula Gap, not only because the place tells the story of giant lava flows and enormous floods, but also because it is so beautiful, whether under blazing summer sun or the infrequent winter snowstorm. Geologically, Wallula Gap is a microcosm of the geology of the Pacific Northwest, especially that of eastern Washington and Oregon.

In terms of the ecology of this area, Wallula Gap is unique. The sagebrush and arrow-leaved balsamroot are typical of much of eastern Washington and Oregon; so are the patches of bunchgrass and scattered juniper trees. But, for the most part, the animals are different: beavers have built dams along the creek in Juniper Canyon; bighorn sheep climb the cliffs; white pelicans and bald eagles fly through the water gap. The story of Wallula Gap would not be complete without including the biology. I asked my friend Mike Denny to write an essay on the biology of the area because he is a walking encyclopedia on the animals (particularly the birds) and plants of the Pacific Northwest. He wrote the essay, offered

Beaver ponds on the floor of Juniper Canyon. The wetland near the bridges resulted from the inundation of the valley's mouth by the reservoir upstream of McNary Dam. (Bob Carson photo)

photographs, added a list of fauna and flora, and also helped me with the road log from Sand Station south of Wallula Gap to the cemetery at Wallula.

The town of Wallula lies on the east bank of the Columbia River just north of Wallula Gap and the mouth of the Walla Walla River. The population of this area is sparse: only farm families and a handful of people at Wallula Junction live close to Wallula Gap. For such a tiny town, Wallula has had quite a history. The goals of early settlers to make it big were never realized, and Wallula, as with many other small towns in the dam-building era of the 20th century, had to move because of a rising reservoir. My colleague G. Thomas "Tom" Edwards is a scholar of Pacific Northwest history; he has written an essay on the 19th-century history. Our friend

Lawrence "Larry" L. Dodd wrote on the 20th-century history; he, then the archivist of Penrose Memorial Library, lives not too far east of Wallula.

A time gap existed in our record of Wallula and the nearby water gap. More than 12,000 years passed between the surge of the last flood of glacial meltwater and the 1805 arrival of the Lewis and Clark expedition. Catherine Dickson has written an essay on the prehistory of this area; her contribution is a bridge between the natural history and recorded human history.

The beauty of Wallula Gap changes as the sun illuminates first the high western cliffs and then the eastern side. The weather changes from rare rain to occasional snow, from gray clouds to blue skies; the scenery from the green of spring to the brown of autumn,

Two sailboats near the Twin Sisters. (Dianne Kornberg photo)

Two western junipers in front of a miniature Channeled Scabland. (Dianne Kornberg photo)

from dark cliffs to sparkling water. Wanting more and better pictures, I asked my friends Dianne Kornberg, Bob Baker and Kathy Farrell to photograph the gap from end to end.

I was pleased when my colleague Don Snow, a longtime writer for *High Country News*, agreed to write the foreword for this book. Margo Scribner, my friend who teaches writing at Whitman College, edited the entire book, some of it twice.

I am grateful to Whitman College and many of its employees for all the support necessary to write this book. Cora Heid, Patti Moss and Tana Park "typed" the manuscript. Soren Klingsporn, Meghan Mix, Tara Gregg, Savanna Ferguson, Gwen Leslie and Sara Gasparich helped with drafting and photographs. The authors appreciate the assistance of Colleen McFarland, Janet Mallen, Michael Paulus and Bill Huntington in obtaining maps and photographs in the archives of Whitman College's Penrose Memorial

Library. Ron Urban flew me over the Columbia River for aerial photographs of Wallula and the gap.

Fred Mitchell, Bob Bennett, Virgil Reynolds, Chris Hyland and Larry Walker were instrumental in getting photographs of Wallula Gap from years preceding the downriver construction of McNary Dam. Also appreciated are images of paintings by David Manuel from Fred Mitchell.

Friends and colleagues Brennan Jordan and Steve Reidel provided answers to many questions I had about the geology. I am grateful to others for partial and full reviews of the book at various stages. Kevin Pogue provided a detailed review of the chapters on geography and geology just after they were written. Ewart Baldwin, Alex McGregor, Steve Reidel, and Rowland Tabor reviewed the book just before publication. I also learned from geologists Bruce Bjornstad, Jim O'Connor, Pat Spencer, Jay Van Tassell and John Winter. I accept responsibility for any errors or omissions in the book.

All the friendly folks at Keokee Books are a pleasure to work with. Chris Bessler welcomed me into his home as well as his office as we worked on so many issues: cost, color or not, horizontal versus vertical format, etc. Patrick Nash made a beautiful design out of a mess of text from different authors and images from different photographers. I especially appreciate dozens of conversations with editor Billie Jean Plaster from start to finish; she improved the book in countless ways. Thanks are due also to Laura Wahl and Carole Eldridge for their help.

The publication of this book would not have been possible without the help of James Payne of Fort Walla Walla Museum, Steve Gibbons of the National Park Service, Roger Trick of the Whitman Mission National Historic Site and Peter Harvey of Whitman College.

The Twin Sisters and a lone western juniper. (Dianne Kornberg photo)

For funding, I am indebted to the National Natural Landmarks program of the National Park Service; Fort Walla Walla Museum; the George T. Welch Testamentary Trust; the Mary Garner Esary Trust; the Clara and Art Bald Trust; Tourism Walla Walla; the Northwest Interpretative Association; World Wide Travel Service; my mother, Libby Carson; and Whitman College.

The authors appreciate indirect help in completion of the book from the following organizations:

Audubon Washington
Battelle Pacific Northwest National Laboratory (Richland, Washington)
Blue Mountain Audubon Society (Walla Walla, Washington)
Confederated Tribes of the Umatilla Indian Reservation
Ice Age Floods Institute (Richland, Washington)
McNary National Wildlife Refuge
Tri-State Steelheaders (Walla Walla, Washington)
Umatilla National Wildlife Refuge
U.S. Army Corps of Engineers (Walla Walla District)
Walla Walla Basin Watershed Council
Walla Walla Community College
Washington Native Plant Society
Whitman Mission National Historic Site

Wallula Gap is not without threats to its integrity – concerns for humans and concerns for nature. Some of these threats exist elsewhere in the drainage basin of the Columbia River. Why was rock climbing banned at the Twin Sisters, and why is there a fence there? This area was given to the county by the U.S. Army Corps of Engineers for climbing and other recreation and for nature study.

Graffiti on the Twin Sisters is a problem; more visitor use, including rock climbing, would decrease vandalism. The fence along U.S. Highway 730 serves little purpose, as cattle no longer graze there. If the fence remains, a gate is needed to make access easier, particularly for the elderly and handicapped, to the small dune field east of the Twin Sisters. The dunes lie in a depression carved by the floods from Glacial Lake Missoula. The maze of basalt cliffs here is the best example of Channeled Scabland in Walla Walla County.

A second threat comes from irrigators who are considering a dam and reservoir in Juniper Canyon, one of the crown jewels at Wallula Gap. One proposal, with a preliminary cost estimate of $150 million, is for a 320-foot-high dam with a reservoir backing 2.5 miles up the canyon. Water would be pumped from the Columbia River during high flows and released when needed. However, the volume of the reservoir would be a drop in the bucket compared with upstream reservoirs behind Grand Coulee, Dworshak and other dams. In addition, boating recreation potential would be minimal compared with that of immediately adjacent Lake Wallula behind McNary Dam. Juniper Canyon hosts three very different natural communities: a south-facing grassland with basalt outcrops; a valley-floor wetland with beaver dams and a great variety of birds, mammals, reptiles, amphibians, fish and plants; and a north-facing slope with a Missoula floods gravel bar, sand dunes, and many species of shrubs and flowers. What would happen to the ecological, geological and recreation value of this unit of McNary National Wildlife Refuge if filled with a dam, a reservoir, a pipeline and a pumping station? With a giant gravel bar on the south side of the canyon, would the left abutment of the proposed dam leak?

A continuing problem is exotic species, particularly invasive

Rock climber on Twin Sisters. (Bob Carson photo)

plants. Cheatgrass, star thistle, and Russian olive are examples of such plants introduced from Eurasia in the 19th century. Invasive plants are widespread in the Wallula area and elsewhere in the western United States. They outcompete native plants, therefore potentially reducing food and shelter for native animals. Some native animals, however, adapt to the exotic plants. Will exotic species increase in number and range? Will humans be able to control the number and distribution of invasive plants? How will climate change affect exotic species?

The Columbia, similar to every other river, has the potential to be polluted. Consider what is upstream of Wallula. Dioxin can come from a paper mill that is not totally chlorine free. Feedlots and failing liquid waste disposal systems release excess nutrients to shallow aquifers in hydrologic continuity with the Columbia River and its tributaries. Improper disposal of batteries, solvents and many other products results in heavy metals and toxic organics in surface and groundwater. Road deicing chemicals and motor oil wash off roads and into nearby waterways. Thermal pollution may come from power generation and other industry. Radioactivity moves away from the Hanford Nuclear Reservation (currently known as the Hanford Site).

What about the heavy sediment load carried by the Walla Walla River and its tributaries, particularly the Touchet River? Some consider sediment to be the most serious pollutant. Before the construction of McNary, John Day, The Dalles and Bonneville dams, the Columbia River carried this sediment toward the Pacific Ocean. For more than a half century, the Walla Walla River has been building a delta into Lake Wallula. The subaqueous portion of this delta extends west across the reservoir. As the reservoir gets shallower, dredging will probably be required to allow shipping between upriver ports, such as Lewiston, Idaho, and Pasco, Washington, and downriver ports, such as Astoria, Oregon, and Longview, Washington. Would the dredge spoils be toxic? Would dredging result in turbidity? Where would the dredge spoils be placed?

Critical is the long-standing threat to fish in this area. Parked vehicles are a common sight along U.S. Highway 730 through Wallula Gap. For the most part, they belong to folks fishing in the reservoir. For millennia salmon, steelhead and other fish have been caught here and elsewhere in the Columbia River and its tributaries.

What is the future of anadromous fish in the Pacific Northwest? What about dams, habitat, hatcheries, pesticides and overfishing? Were the lower Snake River dams four too many? Will salmon decline and other problems, such as the sediment behind Lower Granite Dam, lead to breaching of the lower Snake River dams?

Two additional concerns involve energy production. The Horse Heaven Hills are crowned by wind turbines from southwest of the Tri-Cities to south of Walla Walla. Some wind turbines (e.g., in California) are known to be killers of birds and bats, and some people (e.g., on Cape Cod, Massachusetts) do not like wind

South abutment of proposed dam in Juniper Canyon. Between the beaver ponds on the valley floor and the basalt buttes at the top is a giant gravel bar deposited by the Missoula floods. Juniper trees and a variety of shrubs grow in the sandy soils of this north-facing slope. (Bob Carson photo)

North abutment of dam proposed for Juniper Canyon. Granitic erratics transported by icebergs riding the Missoula floods are scattered across the basaltic bedrock from the bottom of the canyon to the buttes at the top. The south-facing slope has thin, silty sails and sparse vegetation. (Bob Carson photo)

turbines in their view. On the other hand, wind turbines reduce the need for electricity from fossil fuels, with all their problems, especially global climate change. Fortunately, to date, the builders of wind farms near Wallula Gap have worked with biologists to place turbines in places where bird and bat mortality is minimal. Considering the presence of McNary National Wildlife Refuge, continued cooperation is important.

Second, production of electricity by burning fossil fuels at Wallula has been considered. In 2002, a 1,300-megawatt, natural gas turbine facility was proposed. In 2007, a coal-burning power plant was proposed, with the coal shipped by rail from northeastern Wyoming. The proponents hope that 65 percent of the carbon dioxide produced by the 600- to 700-megawatt power plant could be captured and then stored in basalt flows a mile or so beneath the surface. Many questions need to be answered before fossil fuels are used to generate electricity at the west end of the Walla Walla Valley. What are the indirect costs in terms of air pollution, noise, visibility, acid deposition and global climate change?

Perhaps the greatest threat, not just to Wallula Gap, is global climate change. Increased violent weather may bring more wind energy, but what about other factors? The warmer temperature will increase evaporation, taking more moisture from the soil and putting more water vapor into our atmosphere. But will Wallula get more precipitation or less? There will be fewer winter snowfalls and less ice on the edge of the reservoir. Will it matter to animals that plants bloom earlier? Are there species that will not be able to tolerate hotter summers?

This book is intended for folks to learn about Wallula Gap, an oasis in the desert, a microcosm of Pacific Northwest natural

Fred L. Mitchell and Fred Mitchell Sr. with four sturgeon caught at Port Kelley in about 1945. They are posing in front of the old location of Pete's Sport Shop on North Second Avenue in Walla Walla. (Fred L. Mitchell Collection)

and human history. I hope that the words and photos will help the readers make informed decisions about these potential threats, about public use of public land, about energy, about water and wildlife, about dams and dredging.

Wallula Gap is a treasure for naturalists and hikers. The water gap is one of 17 National Natural Landmarks in Washington. Author Andrea Jarvela wrote in *The Washington Almanac* (Portland: WestWinds Press, 1999): "The National Natural Landmarks Program, established in 1962 by the U.S. secretary of the interior, identifies and encourages the protection of sites in the United States that contain the best examples of geological and ecological components of the nation's landscape." Of the 14 National Natural Landmarks in eastern Washington, 12 are geological, with seven related to glaciation and related megafloods. At this writing, a bill

Fishing at Wallula while there is high water on the Columbia River. (Fred L. Mitchell Collection)

establishing the Ice Age Floods National Geologic Trail is working its way through the U.S. Congress. Wallula Gap is an essential part of this geologic trail that prehistoric floods took from Montana to the Pacific Ocean.

The students of almost every geology and environmental studies class I teach go to Wallula Gap for an afternoon. These students are not only youngsters from Whitman College but also folks my age and older from the Quest program at Walla Walla Community College. We study the rocks, the landforms, the vegetation. We climb to dunes blown by the Prevailing Westerlies and to perched eddy bars deposited by ancient floods 900 feet deep. We discuss the wetlands created by beaver dams and McNary Dam and hope that another dam and reservoir will not drown Juniper Canyon.

I thank all those who have accompanied me to Wallula Gap for more than three decades. It is a special place to my family and my students – for hiking, for wildlife, for geology and for scenery. My sons learned to rock climb at the Twin Sisters; we hope the ban on climbing there will end. In particular, I thank Clare for exploring the gap with me, taking photographs, and identifying birds and flowers; I value our time together there. Finally, appreciative of the love, support and encouragement of my mother, Libby (1917-2008), I dedicate this book to her.

–Bob Carson

Looking southwest across the Two Sisters and down the Columbia River at sunset. (John Clement photo)

I

Introduction:
Why is the Wallula Area Special?

Robert J. Carson and Lawrence L. Dodd

"The country on both sides is high, dry prairie plains without a stick of timber."

–Patrick Gass, 1811, *Journal of the Voyages and Travels of a Corps of Discovery*

Imagine that you are with a party of Wanapums, American Indians with villages in central Washington, canoeing down the Columbia River late one autumn in the 18th century. Your journey started near Sentinel Gap; one canoe almost overturned at Priest Rapids. A few nights ago you camped on one of several large islands north of present-day Richland, Washington. To the east of this island are bluffs of sedimentary strata hundreds of feet high; to the west are sand dunes. There are no reactors; no highways or railroads; no windmills, utility wires or irrigation pumps; no orchards, vineyards or tree farms; no cities; no cattle; and no dams.

As you drift and paddle south, the bluffs to the east taper to nothing. For two days' voyage the land near the river is very low, with sagebrush on sandy soil. To the southwest is a line of hills rising 1,000 feet above the river (one is present-day Badger Mountain). Just after the Columbia's course changes from southerly to easterly, the Yakima River joins on the right. The Yakima is the medium-sized of three tributaries joining the Columbia in the Pasco Basin. You may be puzzled that the Columbia is taking you east, because there is a plan to rendezvous with Chinooks from the West Coast.

Soon after the river starts to turn south again, the largest of the three tributaries, the Snake River, joins from the left. As the Columbia turns more southerly, the hills to the southwest get closer and then hug the western shore. Soon the tiny Walla Walla River, the smallest of the three tributaries, enters from the east. One Wanapum states that his father met here with the Nez Perce. This is where Lewis and Clark will camp with your descendants. This is where inland tribes will bargain with fur-trading companies; this is where the town of Wallula will be sited, in the southeast corner of the Pasco Basin.

View toward the Columbia River from just east of the Twin Sisters. The photographer of this century-old scene is unknown. (Whitman College and Northwest Archives)

Contrast the flood-eroded cliffs with the smooth, loess-covered hilltops. (Bob Carson photo)

Top: Wallula Gap before McNary Dam, view south-southeast. Other than roads and railroads along the shores, this oblique aerial photograph taken in the early 1950s shows the Columbia River about how it appeared to American Indians. The Twin Sisters are in left-center. **Bottom:** In this early 1950s oblique air photo taken toward the north, the Twin Sisters are in right-center, with the mouth of the Walla Walla River behind them. In the distance is the Pasco Basin. The river looked about the same as when the Lewis and Clark expedition reached here in October 1805. (Army Corps of Engineers photos)

Ahead is Wallula Gap, where the mighty river cuts through the Horse Heaven Hills. You may wonder about the increase in the Columbia's velocity, or why there are now cliffs rising nearly 1,000 feet above both sides of the river. Is it just because the gods made Mother Earth that way? Two distinct rock towers on the east arouse your curiosity. As the canoes drift along, the oldest member of your party explains the origin of the two towers. She relates how Coyote turned two sisters to stone:

"The large basalt pillars in front of you are actually two Cayuse Indian sisters. Coyote, a spiritual hero of many Indian legends, fell in love with three sisters who were building a trap in the river to catch salmon. Always the trickster, coyote watched them and at night he would destroy their work. The sisters rebuilt the trap daily but coyote would destroy it each time. One morning coyote saw the sisters crying. They were starving for fish. Coyote promised to build them a trap if they would become his wives. The sisters consented and he kept his promise. For many years Coyote lived happily with the sisters but after a while he became jealous of them. Using his supernatural powers, coyote changed two of his wives into basalt pillars. The third wife he turned into a cave downstream. He then turned into a rock so that he could watch over them forever" (story taken from the interpretive sign on U.S. Highway 730 at the Twin Sisters).

Coyote turned the Twin Sisters to stone. (Bob Baker photo)

You are fascinated by the explanation and ask the old woman to tell more stories at camp this evening. The sun reflects from the water right in front of you, making it difficult to see which channel has the fewest rocks and logs to avoid. As the river slowly swings west, the sun also moves west and sinks, making visibility worse. There's a wind from the southwest this evening; the temperature drops below freezing.

A break in the cliffs appears ahead on the left. A tiny creek comes out of a big side canyon. The willows and cottonwoods along the creek have lost their leaves. A few juniper trees stand on the north-facing slope of the canyon, and abundant bunchgrass covers the south-facing slope. You paddle the canoes to the shore at a place now called Juniper Canyon, set up camp on a sand bar at the mouth of the little creek, and build a fire with the abundant wood. The elders report that beaver and deer live up the canyon, that fishing for salmon is good here, and that many birds nest on the island between here and the cliffs on the other side of the river.

After eating, your party sits around the small fire. The old woman who told the legend of the Twin Sisters tells other stories. She tells about the great flood, when large mammals and huge icebergs topped a raging torrent that killed almost all her ancestors thousands of moons ago. She tells about the time many hundreds of moons ago that the sky was dark for days and fine snow fell on all the land – snow that would not melt. She tells of the Bridge of the Gods in the much larger gorge many days' journey ahead (the Bridge of the Gods likely formed hundreds of years ago at Bonneville when a great earthquake triggered a landslide that temporarily dammed the Columbia River).

You ask the old woman why this gorge is here, why the lowland to the north changed into this canyon. She says that it has something to do with Coyote. You ask her why the river makes this great bend, why it ever went east if it's trying to reach the sea. How could it turn toward, cross and cut through these rocks. Why the great bend of the Columbia River? Why Wallula Gap? She shakes her head.

In the morning your party shoves off and continues downriver toward the rendezvous. You have many more days to travel, fighting a headwind. Shortly after you leave Juniper Canyon, the cliff heights diminish; the Columbia has entered the Umatilla Basin. Starting with the Umatilla Rapids, the canoeists have much white water even before they reach Celilo Falls. Three tributaries – the Umatilla, the John Day and the Deschutes – will enter the river from the south before the Wanapums arrive at the Columbia River Gorge. Will the Cayuse here be friend or foe?

•••

This land and these rivers have always been sacred to American Indians. The Columbia River provides many blessings, including water, salmon and transportation. To those who use or study rivers, certain parts are particularly interesting, such as the headwaters, the mouth, canyons and waterfalls. Celilo Falls is drowned behind The Dalles Dam, but Wallula Gap is still with us; McNary Dam inundated only the bottom 40 feet.

The Columbia River at the mouth of Juniper Canyon. Canoes have been replaced with roads and railroads, tugs and barges. (Bob Carson photo)

View south from the Pasco Basin past Wallula Gap to the Umatilla Basin. The Columbia River flows through the water gap cut across the Horse Heaven Hills. Behind the irrigated fields, from right to left, are the town of Wallula, the delta of the Walla Walla River and the grain elevators at Wallula Junction. (Bob Carson photo)

Facts About the Columbia River

Source: Columbia Lake, southeastern British Columbia, Canada (elevation 2,655 feet)

Mouth: near Astoria, Oregon, and Ilwaco, Washington

Length (source to mouth): 1,450 miles* (the 12th longest in the United States)

Average discharge (at mouth): 265,000 cubic feet per second (the second highest in the United States, after Mississippi-Ohio-Missouri river system)

Drainage area: 258,000 square miles* (the sixth largest in the United States)

Number of dams on main stem: 14*

Number of major dams in drainage basin: 219*

* including Canada

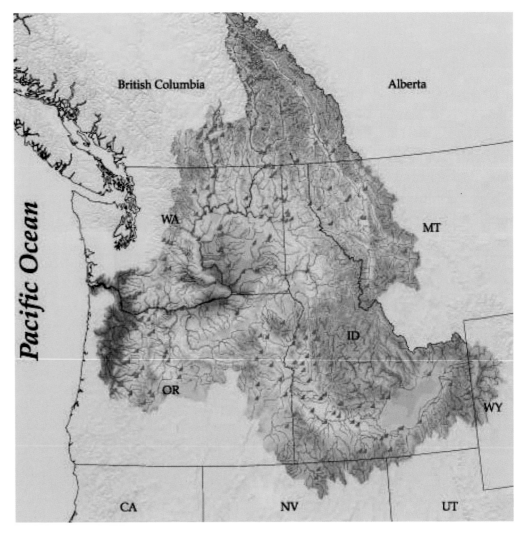

Shaded relief map of the Columbia River drainage basin. Elevations increase from green to red. The red triangles are 219 major dams. Wallula Gap is where the Washington-Oregon state line intersects the Columbia River. (Washington Department of Ecology, Southwest Washington Coastal Erosion Study)

Just north of Wallula Gap and the mouth of the Walla Walla River is the town of Wallula, Washington. To the 227 citizens of Wallula (2000 census), and to many people before them, this place is also special. American Indians and explorers such as Lewis and Clark camped here. In the 19th century, Wallula and Walla Walla were rivals for business and population; both outcompeted Pasco, Kennewick and Richland, Washington, upstream as well as Umatilla, Oregon, downstream.

Wallula Gap is a water gap where the Columbia River slices through the Horse Heaven Hills. These hills are an anticlinal ridge that stretches east-west along the border of Washington and Oregon. An anticline is a long, narrow upfold of rocks; at Wallula Gap the rocks are basalt flows that originated from the east. Here the Columbia, one of the largest rivers in North America, cuts across the ridge of young lava flows, just as the Delaware River cut across a ridge of old sandstone beds to form the Delaware Water Gap between Pennsylvania and New Jersey. Until 1953, the Columbia River flowed relatively quickly south through Wallula Gap, from Washington's Pasco Basin to Oregon's Umatilla Basin; today the reservoir slows the water's velocity.

Twenty million years ago, there were no basalt flows here; perhaps there was granite.

Twenty million years ago, there was not the ridge of the Horse Heaven Hills here; perhaps the landscape was flat.

Fifteen million years ago, this place was not a desert. There was a subtropical forest growing on soils similar to those in the Amazon Basin.

Fifteen million years ago, there was no Wallula Gap; the Columbia River was far to the west. The Clearwater-Salmon River, not a tributary to the Snake River at that time, was far to the north. The Snake River was who-knows-where other than southern Idaho. Hells Canyon did not exist.

Fifteen thousand years ago, what many geologists believe were the Earth's largest floods raced through Wallula Gap. The gap was only large enough to accommodate perhaps half of the discharge of floods from Montana's Glacial Lake Missoula. So water surged through the gap at a rate of 8 or 10 cubic miles per hour, at a velocity of perhaps 40 to 50 miles per hour.

Fifteen thousand years ago, humans were not here. A continental ice sheet stretching from British Columbia to Greenland blocked the way from the Bering land bridge to northwestern North America. Tidewater glaciers calved icebergs from the south coast of Alaska to the northwest coast of Washington. Scientists debate how American Indians got to the Pacific Northwest. Did they walk an ice-free corridor from the Yukon through Alberta to Montana? Did they boat from Alaska along the coast of British Columbia to Washington? Or did American Indians arrive by some very different route?

For more than half a century there has not been a river here. The water gap was partially drowned by McNary Dam; construction started in 1947, and the power units went into operation from 1953 to 1957. When the reservoir was filled to 63 billion cubic feet (almost more than half a cubic mile) in 1953, the water level rose from about 300 feet to 340 feet above sea level. The Columbia River became Lake Wallula.

Before the reservoir was created, road and rail traffic passed through Wallula Gap. Long before that, American Indian canoes and then steamboats used the Columbia River. The locks and dams on

Chief Yellepit trades a white horse for William Clark's sword. This oil painting by David Manuel shows the exchange of April 28, 1806, taking place north of the mouth of the Walla Walla River. The journals of Lewis and Clark indicate that this event occurred on the west side of Wallula Gap. (Fred L. Mitchell Collection, with permission from the Manuel family, Hot Lake Springs, LaGrande, Oregon)

The Lewis & Clark Expedition in the Wallula Area

(after Moulton, 1991, and Fifer, 2002)

Cmpsite	Date	Activity
WESTWARD BOUND		
Present location of Sacagawea State Park southeast of Pasco	October 16, 1805	Reached mouth of Snake River, canoeing from near Fishhook Park
	October 17, 1805	Clark went about 10 miles up Columbia River to mouth of Yakima River
East bank of Columbia River south of confluence with Walla Walla River	October 18, 1805	Canoed down "the great Columbia" to Wallula Gap; may have seen snow-capped Mount Hood
South bank of Columbia River near mouth of Umatilla River	October 19, 1805	Canoed through Wallula Gap and into Umatilla Basin
EASTWARD BOUND		
Yellepit, on west bank of Columbia River near north end of Wallula Gap	April 27, 1806	Hiked from campsite near Plymouth, Washington
	April 28, 1806	Wallula Chief Yellepit gave Clark a white horse; Clark gave the chief his sword
Wallula, north of mouth of Walla Walla River	April 29, 1806	Ferried baggage and swam horses east across Columbia River
Touchet River upstream of town of Touchet, near Eureka Flat	April 30, 1806	Hiked northeast toward valley of Touchet River

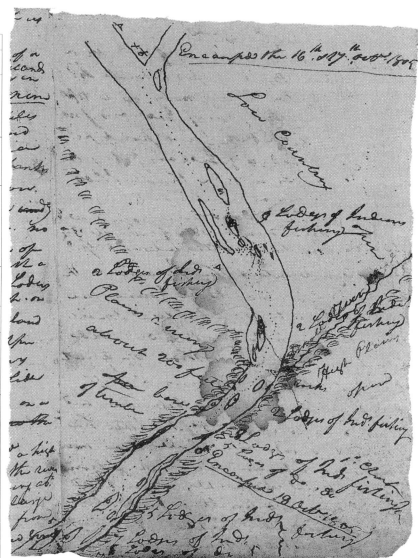

Map of the Columbia River near the mouth of the Walla Walla River, from *The Definitive Journals of Lewis and Clark*, 1805 (Moulton 1991). (Missouri History Museum)

the Columbia and Snake rivers now allow tugs and barges to go from the ports of Astoria, Longview and Portland to the ports of Pasco and Walla Walla near the mouth of the Snake River, and the ports of Lewiston and Clarkston near the mouth of the Clearwater River. Sailboats take advantage of usually windy Wallula Gap and tie up at the yacht club next to the grain elevators at Port Kelley.

What changes there have been since Lewis and Clark paddled through Wallula Gap in October 1805 and then camped at the mouth of the Walla Walla River in April 1806! Their campsite is under water; nearby stand grain elevators at Wallula Junction. To the north, steam rises from a pulp and paper mill. Rows of hybrid poplar trees grow rapidly on a giant farm, and rows of small trees and big vines form orchards and vineyards. A feedlot surrounds a meat packing plant. There are plans for fossil fuels to generate electricity at Wallula.

On the Horse Heaven Hills just east and west of Wallula Gap rise hundreds of windmills. American Indians would have been impressed by their size (more than 240 feet high, including the blades); these quiet machines might even have been sacred. The windmills are compatible with birds, kangaroo rats, cattle grazing and wheat growing.

The development at the town of Wallula is greater than that just to the south of Wallula Gap, where huge pumps on the shore of Lake Wallula send water uphill for irrigation. At the reservoir's edge, folks camp on sandbars that are tiny compared to those that existed when the Columbia River was free-flowing and transported huge amounts of sediment through the gap. The sand and gravel were temporarily stored in islands between channels and in bars along

Boise Pulp and Paper Mill at night. (Bob Carson photo)

Grain elevators at Wallula Junction. (Dianne Kornberg photo)

the river's edge. The wind blew sand from the Umatilla Basin into Juniper Canyon and from the river bars to the Twin Sisters, forming dunes at both sites. The rising reservoir drowned the river bars, however, cutting off the sand supply to some of the dunes.

The filling of the reservoir also drowned the floodplain and associated wetlands, drastically decreasing the area of riparian habitat. But by good fortune, the 340-foot level of Lake Wallula happened to create three new wetlands by drowning parts of former or existing valleys. Two wetlands are parts of McNary National Wildlife Refuge – one in an old river or flood channel north of Wallula, the other along the lower Walla Walla River. The third, new wetland, in lower Juniper Canyon (mostly Bureau of Land Management property), is partly due to dozens of beaver dams across the creek.

Wallula Gap is an oasis in the desert of eastern Washington and Oregon. From end to end and top to bottom, there are only two residences. The vegetation immediately adjacent to water (for example, in Juniper Canyon) differs completely from the rest of the vegetation. Wallula Gap is part of a desert, yet there are beavers. Wallula Gap has no mountains, yet there are bighorn sheep. The bedrock is all basalt, yet there are granitic boulders. In this book we explore this special place where a mighty river incised resistant rocks, where Lewis and Clark and others made discoveries, and where you can continue the exploration.

Wind turbines cross the Horse Heaven Hills beyond Lake Wallula. (Kathryn Farrell photo)

(John Clement photo)

Chimney Rock
Patterson Head
Two Virgins
Twin Pillars
Castle Rocks
Cayuse Sisters
McKenzie and Ross Rocks
Hell's Smoke Stacks
Twin Captains

The Twin Sisters

On the east bank of Wallula Gap are two, highly visible scabs of basalt surviving erosion by the Missoula floods. American Indians, voyageurs, explorers, missionaries, artists, photographers, travelers and settlers have identified these geologic features with a variety of names: Twin Sisters, Two Sisters, Twin Captains, Twin Pillars, Twins, The Twins, Two Captains, McKenzie and Ross Rocks, Ross-McKenzie Rocks, Cayuse Sisters, Rocks of the Kye-use Girls, The Two Virgins, Castle Rocks, Chimney Rock, Chimney Rocks, Pillars, Hell's Smoke Stacks, and Patterson Head. The presence of the Twin Sisters in a thousand-foot-deep gorge along the Columbia River has caused the pioneers and others to write about the two erosion remnants; following are their remarks spanning more than a century.

The miniature channeled scabland on the east side of northern Wallula Gap. This Arnold photo from the 1930s shows the Columbia River at low water behind the Twin Sisters. (Fred L. Mitchell Collection)

Reverend Samuel Parker (1779-1866), American missionary in Oregon Country, 1835

"Two thirds of the way down this deep channel are two high eminences called the Pillars, to which, by a circuitous route, I descended. They stand upon conical bases, eighty or a hundred feet high above the river; and above these bases rise nearly a hundred feet perpendicular. They are indeed remarkable; but there are so many singular formations in this volcanic country, that curiosities become common."

–Samuel Parker, 1846, *Journal of an Exploring Tour Beyond the Rocky Mountains*, p. 281

James W. Nesmith (1820-85), U.S. senator and U.S. congressman, October 10, 1843

"Our camp is quite a picturesque place. Immediately under the high bluffs of the far-famed Columbia, about one-half mile above are two rocks rising 100 feet above the level of the river. They are separated by a small space, and are nearly round, presenting the appearance of two towers. Mr. McKinley [Archibald McKinley was chief factor at Fort Walla Walla from 1841-46] informed me that the Indians looked upon them with a great deal of veneration, and say that they are two Indian damsels, Petrified. I must confess that their appearance does not correspond very well with the tradition."

–Cited by Nesmith Ankeny (a descendant of James W. Nesmith), 1953, *The West As I Knew It*, p. 29

Captain J.C. Frémont (1813-90), American military officer and explorer, between October 25 and 28, 1843

"The sketch [Hill of Columnar Basalt on the Columbia River] of a rock which we passed in the course of the morning is annexed, to show the manner in which the basaltic rock, which constitutes the geological formation of the Columbia valley, now presents itself."

–John C. Frémont, 1845, *Report of the Exploring Expedition of the Rocky Mountains in the Year 1842, and to Oregon and North California in the Years 1843-'44*, p. 184

Paul Kane (1810-71), painter, famous for his paintings of First Nations peoples in the Canadian West, July 11, 1847

"As we approached the place where the Walla-Walla debauches into the Columbia River, we came in sight of two extraordinary rocks projecting from a high steep cone or mound about 700 feet above the level of the river. These are called by the voyageurs the Chimney Rocks, and from their being visible from a great distance they are very serviceable as landmarks. Sketch No. 13 represents one of them and the cone. … The Walla-Walla Indians called these the 'Rocks of the Kye-use [*sic*] girls.' "

–Paul Kane, 1925, *Wanderings of an Artist among the Indians of North America, from Canada to Vancouver's Island and Oregon, Through the Hudson's Bay Company's Territory and Back Again*, p. 185

TWIN SISTERS OF THE COLUMBIA

The National Archives

"The Gate of the Columbia as seen from Fort Walla Walla, showing Ross Peak, McKenzie Peak and the 'Chimney Rock' as seen from the east." Sketched by G. Sohon.

Courtesy the National Archives.

Above: Old postcard. (Robert A. Bennett Collection) **Opposite page, from left:** John Frémont's report published in 1845 included this sketch, and Paul Kane's book published posthumously in 1925 included this artwork. In his book, Kane related that the Coyote legend was told to him "by an Indian whilst I was sketching this extraordinary scene." The Indian identified Coyote as "the great medicine wolf of the Columbia River." In J. Russell Harper's book, *Paul Kane's Frontier*, 1971, p. 295, appears a list of four Kane drawings of Chimney Rocks: a woodcut (as appeared in *Wanderings*, p. 113), two pencil drawings, and an oil on canvas. (Whitman College and Northwest Archives)

Alexander Ross (1783-1856), Canadian fur trader, 1855

"On the south the prospect is romantic, and abruptly checked by a striking contrast of wild hills and rugged bluffs on either side of the water, and rendering particularly so by two singular towering rocks similar in colour, shape and height called by the natives 'Twins' situated on the east side."

–K.A. Spaulding, ed., 1956, *The Fur Hunters of the Far West*, p. 119

Captain John Mullan's 1858 Map of Military Reconnaissance identifies the location of "McKenzie's Peak" and "Chimney Rock" (Twin Sisters), and across the Columbia River (west side of Wallula Gap) is "Ross's Peak." The high bluffs on either side of Wallula Gap were named for Donald McKenzie, who was in charge of the construction of the 1818 Fort Nez Perce, and Alexander Ross, who was in charge of Fort Nez Perce between 1818 and 1823. (B.C. Payette, compiler, 1968, *Captain John Mullan; His Life*, p. 198)

Captain John Mullan (1830-1909), Army engineer who constructed Mullan Road, July 21, 1858

"We have this day a fine view of the Gap of the Columbia near old Wallah Wallah where are situated the well defined 'Ross's and McKenzie's Peaks,' on opposite banks of the river."

–John Mullan, 1858, *Journal from Fort Dalles to Fort Walla Walla*, p. 6

John H. Williams, author and publisher, 1912
"The grim sentinels of 'the Wallula Gateway,' huge basaltic pillars that rise on the south bank of the river, where it crosses the Washington-Oregon line."

–John H. Williams, 1912, *The Guardians of the Columbia*, p. 53

Lewis R. Freeman (1878-1960), American explorer, journalist and war correspondent, 1921
"The double-topped butte, an outstanding landmark for voyageurs for a hundred years, has long been called 'The Two Virgins.' The story is told locally of a Catholic priest who saved his life by taking refuge in a cave between the castellated turrets during an Indian massacre, but who got in rather serious trouble with the Church afterwards as a consequence of sending words of his deliverance by a French-Canadian half-breed voyageur. The latter got the salient details of the story straight but neglected to explain that the two

virgins were mountains. The result was that the unlucky priest narrowly missed excommunication for saving his life at the expense of breaking his vows. I got no affidavit with the story, but local 'stock' yarns are always worth preserving on account of their color."

–Lewis R. Freeman, ed., 2001, *Down the Columbia*, p. 229

M.J. Lorraine, explored the Columbia River from its source to its mouth alone in a rowboat, October 16, 1921
"Immediately on entering the hills a noticeable butte is seen on the left shore. This is the Twin Sisters, crowned with two almost equal-sized turret-shaped summits."

–M.J. Lorraine, 1924, *The Columbia Unveiled*, p. 324

Far left: Three Navy planes over the Twin Sisters, identified as primary trainers made by Stearman, in the N2S series. The planes were most likely based at Naval Air Station, Pasco, Washington, which formed in 1942; the Stearman PT-13 Kaydet appeared late in World War II. (Fred L. Mitchell Collection) **Left:** Looking at the Twin Sisters to the southwest. (Fred L. Mitchell Collection)

Albert and Jane Salisbury, authors, 1950
"Just below the junction of the Walla Walla with the Columbia, these two landmarks looked down on Chief Yellept's [*sic*] village across the big river. Lewis and Clark saw them on both the westward passage and the return trip. Too bad they weren't named the Two Captains."
—Albert and Jane Salisbury, 1950, *Two Captains West*, p. 160

The Seattle Sunday Times Rotogravure, April 16, 1950
The caption "Cannon-Hunters Visit Old Fort" appeared under the 1853 John Mix Stanley drawing of the third Fort Walla Walla (Fort Nez Percés), followed by, "At left can be seen two monument-shaped rocks called the Twin Sisters, which actually are one behind the other, but which the artist drew in this way." (See drawing on page 126.)

Walla Walla Union-Bulletin, June 9, 1955
Includes an article regarding the naming of the columnar rocks as "Two Captains." The article contains a list of names previously used: Twin Sisters, Ross-McKenzie Rocks, Twin Captains, The Twins and Patterson Head.

Walla Walla Union-Bulletin, June 11, 1955
Includes an article about the dedication of the two columnar rocks as the "Two Captains," a memorial to Captain Meriwether Lewis and Captain William Clark. The Washington State Lewis and Clark Sesquicentennial Committee and the District Development Committee of the Walla Walla Chamber of Commerce, in conjunction with the Washington State Parks and Recreation Committee, undertook this movement.

Lee Robinson and friends spent many days in the 1920s exploring and rock climbing at Wallula Gap. (Virgil Reynolds Collection)

Donald B. Church, son of W.D. Church and early resident of Wallula, in recording his boyhood recollections, 1981
"The Twin Sisters, those noble volcanic columns that have stood through the ages in the Wallula Gap" are "a landmark to all who have ever passed this way." Donald, his brother Bob, and sister Betty climbed the south sister. "On the backside of the South one is a natural 'Chimney' or channel which we were able to use to climb all the way to the top. … The rewards when we got to the top were great. … If you listened with your inner ear, you could hear the Song of the Ages, and worship in our humble way, the Great Spirit as the Indians called Him, who created it all!" (Church Collection, Whitman College and Northwest Archives)

In 1978, supported by the Walla Walla Valley Pioneer and Historical Society, a member of said society undertook researching the names given to the two Wallula Gap columnar-jointed towers. It was deemed inappropriate to keep the "Two Captains" name, for the two explorers, Meriwether Lewis and William Clark, did not mention these buttes in their journals. Also, a number of sites along the explorers' route had been named in honor of the Lewis and Clark expedition. It seemed appropriate to return to a name used by local residents and in the American Indian legend. A report was submitted to the Washington State Board of Geographic Names recommending the name "Twin Sisters." In 1979 both the Washington State and the U.S. Boards of Geographic Names officially adopted the name "Twin Sisters."

Bibliography

Clark, Robert, 1995, *River of the West: A chronicle of the Columbia*: New York, Picador USA, 406 p.

Committee on Water Resources Management, Instream Flows, and Salmon Survival in the Columbia River Basin, National Research Council, 2004, *Managing the Columbia River: Instream flows, water withdrawals, and salmon survival*: Washington, D.C., The National Academies Press, 268 p.

Dietrich, William, 1995, *Northwest passage: the great Columbia River*: New York, Simon & Schuster, 448 p.

Fifer, Barbara, 2002, *Day-by-day with the Lewis & Clark Expedition, 1804-1806*: Helena, Montana, Farcountry Press, 36 p.

Gass, Patrick, 1811, *Journal of the voyages and travels of a corps of discovery, under the command of Capt. Lewis and Capt. Clark of the Army of the United States, from the mouth of the River Missouri through the interior parts of North America to the Pacific Ocean, during the years 1804, 1805 and 1806*: Philadelphia, Printed for M. Carey, 262 p.

Harden, Blaine, 1996, *A river lost: The life and death of the Columbia*: New York, W.W. Norton & Company, 271 p.

Heat-Moon, W.L., 1999, *River-horse: The logbook of a boat across America*: Boston, Houghton Mifflin, p. 463-502.

Hockenberry, John, 2001, *A river out of Eden: a novel*: New York, Doubleday, 364 p.

Lang, W.L. and R.C. Carriker, eds., 1999, *Great river of the West: Essays on the Columbia River*: Seattle, University of Washington Press, 181 p.

Leslie, G.A., 2008, "The natural history of Juniper Canyon, Oregon": Walla Walla, Washington, Whitman College, B.A. thesis, 52 p.

Lichatowich, Jim, 1999, *Salmon without rivers: A history of the Pacific salmon crisis*: Washington, D.C., Island Press, 317 p.

Mighetto, Lisa, and W.J. Ebel, 1994, *Saving the salmon: A history of the U.S. Corps of Engineers' efforts to protect anadromous fish on the Columbia and Snake rivers*: Seattle, Historical Research Associates, 262 p.

Miklancic, F.J., 1989, "McNary Dam," *in* R.W. Galster, ed., *Engineering geology in Washington*: Washington Division of Geology and Earth Resources Bulletin 78, v. 1, p. 359-364.

Moulton, G.E., ed., 1991, *The definitive journals of Lewis & Clark*: Lincoln, Nebraska, University of Nebraska Press, v. 5 (Through the Rockies to the Cascades), 415 p.; v. 7 (From the Pacific to the Rockies), 383 p.

Nisbet, Jack, 2005, *The mapmaker's eye: David Thompson on the Columbia Plateau*: Pullman, Washington: Washington State University Press, 180p.

Palmer, Tim, 1997, *The Columbia: Sustaining a modern resource*: Seattle, The Mountaineers, 144 p.

Ulrich, Roberta, 2007, *Empty nets: Indians, dams, and the Columbia*: Corvallis, Oregon, Oregon State University Press, 264 p.

White, Richard, 1995, *The organic machine: The remaking of the Columbia River*: New York, Hill and Wang, 130 p.

View east toward the Twin Sisters from atop the Horse Heaven Hills above Yellepit. The Blue Mountains are in the distance on the right. (John Clement photo)

2

Geography:
An Oasis in the Desert

Robert J. Carson

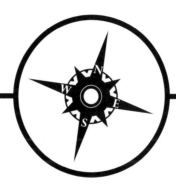

"On approaching Wallawalla the scenery becomes grand: the country is broken into volcanic peaks, forming many fantastic shapes, resembling figures and colossal heads: many of them are seen either insulated or in groups; some of them are known under the name of the Nine-pins. Through this pass of volcanic rocks the wind rushes with great violence in summer, to supply the rarefied portion above. The current had increased very considerably: it often became necessary for the voyageurs to take a pipe, or in other words, a rest."

–Charles Wilkes, 1845, *Narrative of the United States Exploring Expedition*

Wallula Gap lies about halfway between the Cascade Range and the Rocky Mountains. The eastern side of the gap is on the Washington-Oregon state line. However, the west side, the inside of a giant bend of the Columbia River, is all in Washington territory. The Columbia free-flows southeast from Priest Rapids Dam into the Pasco Basin, then turns south past Wallula and the mouth of the Walla Walla River, and swings west toward McNary Dam in the Umatilla Basin.

Wallula Gap is characterized by cliffs cut by the Columbia River as it incised the Horse Heaven Hills (some refer to that portion of the Horse Heaven Hills that lies east of Wallula Gap as the Oregon Hills). To the north, Wallula Gap ends abruptly at the Olympic-Wallowa lineament (see chapter 3 on geology, "Fire and Flood Along the Columbia"), which separates the Pasco Basin to the north from the Horse Heaven Hills. The Horse Heaven Hills stretch

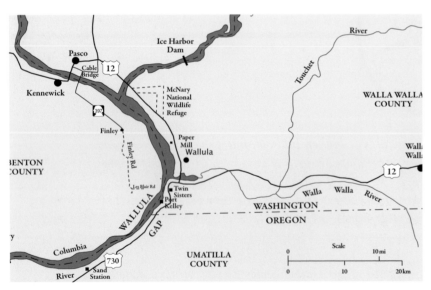

Wallula Gap and vicinity, with portions of Benton, Franklin, Umatilla and Walla Walla counties.

from the Cascades to the Blue Mountains, blocking drainage going from north to south, except where the Columbia River goes through Wallula Gap. The southwest end of Wallula Gap is indefinite but is herein defined as where U.S. Highway 730 passes over the railroad tracks. To the southwest the topography is subdued, like that of the Umatilla Basin. Using these southwest and north ends of the gap as described, its length is 10 miles, extending from just south of River Mile 304 to just south of River Mile 314. (River Miles are distances from the mouth of the Columbia River.)

The "floor" of Wallula Gap, formerly the floodplain of the Columbia River, has an elevation of approximately 300 feet. The river had one, two or three channels in various places on the floodplain. The islands between the channels rose as high as 30 feet above the river level, a little more during droughts, and much less during floods. Today the "floor" of Wallula Gap is at 340 feet, the elevation of the surface of Lake Wallula, the reservoir behind McNary Dam, where the river drops about 75 feet to another reservoir behind John Day Dam. According to topographic maps published from 1962 to 1966, the maximum depth of Lake Wallula is 103 feet at the southwest end of Wallula Gap and 91 feet at the north end. In the half century since the reservoir was created, sediment has no doubt reduced these water depths.

The crest of the east-west trending Horse Heaven Hills is lowest at Wallula Gap, which is why the river chose this place to break through the ridge (see chapter 3). Cliffs on the west side of the gap rise to a maximum elevation of 1,160 feet (the cliff just southwest of Palmer Pond is visible across the river from where U.S. Highway 730 crosses the state line). Elevations rise to the west: 1,430 feet at less than a mile and a half from the river, and 1,760 feet at six miles from the river. Cliffs on the east side of Wallula Gap rise as high as 1,340 feet (above the grain elevators and yacht club at Port Kelley); this is 1,000 feet above Lake Wallula! Elevations on the crest of the Horse Heaven Hills (locally called the Oregon Hills between here and Athena/Weston) rise to the east: 1,560 feet at less than a mile and a half from the river, and 1,813 feet at less than four miles from the river.

A man stands on a gravel bar at the mouth of the Walla Walla River in March 1922. The Twin Sisters are visible beneath the eastern (left) basalt cliffs. Note the rock ledge extending west from near the eastern cliffs; a bridge across the Columbia River was considered at this location. (McFadden Photo Shop)

These cliffs on the west side of the north end of Wallula Gap rise to 1,147 feet, more than 800 feet above the reservoir. The lower slopes are talus, loose rock that has fallen from the basalt cliffs above. (Bob Carson photo)

View north from highest cliffs on the east side of Wallula Gap. Behind the grain elevators at Port Kelley is the Walla Walla Yacht Club. In the distance is the Boise Pulp and Paper Mill at Wallula. (Bob Carson photo)

Geographic Features in the Vicinity of Wallula Gap

There are few named features in or just south of Wallula Gap. There are more people and more industry just to the north.

The east side of Wallula Gap is part of Washington's Walla Walla County and Oregon's Umatilla County. From north to south there are:

1. The town of Wallula, and nearby industry;
2. The mouth of the Walla Walla River, Madame Dorion Park and grain elevators at Wallula Junction;
3. Twin Sisters (Two Sisters on the 1964 topographic map);
4. Port Kelley with grain elevators and a yacht club;
5. Spring Gulch (intermittent stream, private land);
6. Washington-Oregon border (signs);
7. Juniper Canyon (small permanent stream, partly public land);
8. Sand Station on Lake Wallula (Army Corps of Engineers campground and beach three miles southwest of Wallula Gap).

See Road Log, appendix 1, from Sand Station to Wallula.

The west side of the gap is in Benton County, Washington. From north to south, named features are:

1. Yellepit, the end of the road leading southeast from Kennewick;
2. Mound Pond (northeast) and Yellepit Pond (southwest), the largest of many ponds sandwiched between cliffs and a railroad embankment;

3. Switch Pond (northeast) and Palmer Pond (southwest);
4. Spaw Canyon, a small canyon with a private road down from the Horse Heaven Hills almost to the river;
5. Spukshowki Canyon (called Switzer Canyon to the north), across Lake Wallula from Sand Station. This long canyon winds south from the crest of the Horse Heaven Hills.

Mound, Yellepit, Switch and Palmer ponds are the largest of a dozen ponds adjacent to the west shore of Lake Wallula. The east shore has only small ponds between cliffs and U.S. Highway 730. The filling of the reservoir necessitated increasing the elevations of the pre-existing railroads and road. The ponds lie between the sides of Wallula Gap and the embankments for the rails and highway.

Grain elevators at Port Kelley. (Bob Baker photo)

Ponds rest between the railroad tracks beside Lake Wallula and the cliffs on the west side of Wallula Gap. (Bob Carson photo)

Unnamed pond between basalt cliffs and railroad embankment, east of Spaw Canyon on the west side of Wallula Gap. (Bob Carson photo)

Abandoned farm that sits at the rim of the west side of the south end of Wallula Gap. (Bob Carson photo)

A huge vineyard grows east of Spaw Canyon, located at the south end of the western side of Wallula Gap. (Bob Carson photo)

Washington's Pasco Basin

The word "wallula" means meeting of the waters. Northwest of Wallula Gap the Snake River joins the Columbia River in the Pasco Basin. Also entering this lowland are the Yakima River, flowing east from the Cascades, and the Walla Walla River, flowing west from the Blue Mountains. In the vicinity of the mouths of the Yakima and Snake Rivers sit the Tri-Cities: Richland, Kennewick and Pasco. To their northwest lies the extensive Hanford Site of the U.S. Department of Energy.

On the northeast side of the Columbia River, near the mouths of the Snake and Walla Walla rivers, are two small communities, Burbank and Wallula, and the wetlands of McNary National Wildlife Refuge. Major industries include a pulp and paper mill and a nearby fiber farm, meatpacking and an adjacent feedlot, and a refrigerated produce distribution center. Other industries related to biofuels production and electricity generation are operating, and more are planned.

Oregon's Umatilla Basin

After the Columbia River leaves Wallula Gap, it travels southwesterly through the Umatilla Basin. (The Oregon Trail crossed the southern portion of this lowland.) The largest tributary, the Umatilla River, flows northwest from the Blue Mountains, with white water just above its mouth. Towns along the Umatilla River (going downriver) are Echo, Stanfield, Hermiston and Umatilla. To the west, along the Columbia River, are Irrigon and, farther downstream, Boardman. Major facilities in the Umatilla Basin include the Boardman Coal

Plant (Portland General Electric), the Hermiston Generating plant (gas turbines, PG&E Corporation), the Umatilla Chemical Depot (U.S. Army), and, of course, McNary Dam (Army Corps of Engineers). At the east end of the Umatilla Basin are Hat Rock State Park (on Lake Wallula) and Cold Springs Reservoir and National Wildlife Refuge.

Transportation

The only road through Wallula Gap is two-lane U.S. Highway 730, which leads from Interstate Highway 82 at Umatilla to U.S. Highway 12 at Wallula Junction (see Road Log). There are many places to pull off the highway, and camping is permitted at Sand Station and Madame Dorion Park.

Two railroads go the length of Wallula Gap. On the west are the Burlington Northern tracks, used by Amtrak between Portland, Oregon, and Spokane, Washington, via the Tri-Cities. On the east, next to the highway, are the Union Pacific tracks. (The Blue Mountain Railroad Company has a spur line from Wallula to Walla Walla.) Many coal trains use the tracks in Wallula Gap to travel between eastern Wyoming coalfields and the Boardman Coal Plant.

Lake Wallula hosts tugs with barges, fishing boats, sailboats, and an occasional water-skier or sailboarder. As there are locks on the four lower Columbia River dams and the four lower Snake River dams, there is considerable barge traffic between the Portland, Oregon/Longview, Washington, area and the ports in the Tri-Cities area and the Lewiston, Idaho/Clarkston, Washington, area. It is 149 river miles from the north end of Wallula Gap to the junction of the Snake and Clearwater rivers at Lewiston/Clarkston.

U.S. Highway 730 on the east side of Wallula Gap stretches west from Wallula Junction to Interstate Highways 82 and 84 in the Umatilla Basin. (Dianne Kornberg photo)

Railroad tracks line both sides of Lake Wallula. Here on the east are Union Pacific tracks. On the west a train rides the rails of the Burlington Northern. (Kathryn Farrell photo)

Burlington Northern tracks on the west side of Wallula Gap. The cliffs in the distance are near Port Kelley. (Bob Carson photo)

Union Pacific tracks on the east side of Wallula Gap. In the background are cliffs on the west side of the water gap, rising more than 800 feet above the Columbia River. (Bob Carson photo)

Tug pushing barges northeast on Lake Wallula. Note extensive vineyards on loess soils above the basalt cliffs. (Bob Carson photo)

Behind the sailboat is a giant eddy bar deposited by the Missoula floods. The top of the gravel bar is at 900 feet, about 600 feet above the floor of Wallula Gap. (Bob Carson photo)

The fishing boat seems tiny compared to the size of the reservoir. (Dianne Kornberg photo)

Wind surfing on Lake Wallula. (Mike Denny photo)

Weather and Climate

With a latitude of 46 degrees north, Wallula Gap is nearly halfway from the North Pole to the equator. Incidentally, with a longitude of 119 degrees west, the gap is only one degree – about 48 miles at this latitude – short of being one-third of the way around the world from the prime meridian in Greenwich, England. The gap lies in the wind belt called the Prevailing Westerlies (winds are named from whence they come), which actually blow from the southwest, bringing Pacific Ocean moisture and moderate temperatures to the Pacific Northwest. Much of the winter, the moisture and warmth sneak across the Cascades and through the Columbia River Gorge to bring clouds and mild temperatures to the Wallula area. Some of the clouds even dump rain on Wallula Gap, which averages less than 10 inches of precipitation per year. With its southwest-northeast orientation, the Gap is right in line with the Prevailing Westerlies, so the winds are often quite strong here, whipping up big waves on Lake Wallula and making windmills on the Horse Heaven Hills economically (as well as environmentally) a good deal.

Usually the moisture coming from the Pacific Ocean to the Wallula area is insufficient to cause precipitation. There may be fog, particularly if there is a temperature inversion, or clouds without rain or clear skies. Clear, calm days with bright sunshine make Wallula Gap a delightful place for a winter outing.

Hundreds of wind turbines crown the Horse Heaven Hills east and west of Wallula Gap. A small part of Lake Wallula is visible in right-center. (Bob Carson photo)

Clouds rest on the horizon above the east side of Wallula Gap behind Port Kelley. (Bob Carson photo)

Despite the aridity of Wallula, the area occasionally experiences great floods. Winter floods are typically warm rain-on-snow events, whereas summer floods are due to a combination of hot weather, snowmelt and rain. According to the *Walla Walla Union* published on June 24, 1876, the 1876 flood was above the high-water mark of 1862 but lower than the flood of 1832; no discharges are known for these three floods.

The discharges of the December 1964 and February 1996 floods were exceeded at least twice before in historic time. During the flood-of-record in 1894, the Columbia River was above flood stage in Umatilla, just downriver of Wallula Gap, from about May 21 to about July 17; at peak discharge the river was 15 feet above flood stage. The peak discharge (on June 6) at The Dalles, Oregon was 1.24 million cubic feet per second.

At Umatilla the 1948 flood lasted from May 22 to July 4. The deep winter snowfall was followed by heavy rain and high temperatures in late spring. At Vancouver, Washington, the Columbia River flowed at about 1 million cubic feet per second for more than two weeks; at Umatilla the river was more than 11 feet above flood stage for about two weeks.

Occasionally the wind switches to the east or northeast. In winter this brings an "arctic blast" as subfreezing air pushes across the Rockies to the Columbia Basin and even the Pacific Coast. In 1862 the Columbia River froze from Wallula to The Dalles. The Columbia, Snake and Walla Walla rivers froze over in the winter of 1866. Ice covered the Columbia River at Wallula in January 1916.

In the summer easterly winds bring hot, dry air from the mid-continent. Daytime temperatures may exceed 110 degrees Fahrenheit. The heat and low moisture stress the vegetation, especially if strong winds increase evaporation.

Winds may be strong enough to produce dust storms and sandstorms like those reported in the Wallula area in the 19th century. Because of intense agriculture on the Columbia Plateau, large areas lack a cover of vegetation in various places at different times of year. The wind erodes the silty soils, transports the "dust" in dark brown clouds that block the sunlight, and deposits the silt on clothes, windowsills and everything else.

Sandstorms used to be common in the Wallula area but occur less often now that reservoirs have covered the sandbars that the wind attacked. The sandy soils on the central Columbia Plateau are subject to wind erosion. The wind bounces the sand near the ground, so that it may sting your legs without getting in your eyes.

Ice along the east shore of Lake Wallula. (Bob Carson photo)

These two pre-dam photos show the Columbia River at high water, perhaps during the flood of 1948. The left photo was taken from the middle of Wallula Gap, looking southwest toward the Umatilla Basin. The photo on the right was taken from the south end of Wallula Gap and shows the road and railroad on the east side of the Columbia River. (Fred L. Mitchell Collection)

This photo from the 1920s shows the Columbia River floodplain behind the Twin Sisters. The alluvial islands are large because the river's discharge is very low. (Virgil Reynolds Collection)

Old penny postcard titled "A Sand Storm Approaching Pasco, Wash." Actually, a more accurate term might be "dust storm"; most of the sediment in suspension is silt-sized. Windblown sand generally hugs the ground. (Robert A. Bennett Collection)

A dust storm approaches from the the west and fills Wallula Gap. (Kathryn Farrell photo)

The Columbia River at high water in late spring in the 1930s. The trees on the left are at the mouth of the Walla Walla River. (Fred L. Mitchell Collection)

The sand does not travel as high or as far as finer-grained silt and clay.

An interesting meteorological phenomenon, which occurs in the Wallula area and elsewhere in the West, is the chinook or chinook wind. Chinook is an American Indian term meaning "snow eater." Nothing melts snow faster than this warm, dry wind that

Approximate Climate at Wallula Gap		
(after Phillips, 1970)		
Minimum temperature	< -20° F	
Maximum temperature	> 110° F	
Approximate daily temperature range	winter	15° F
	summer	35° F
Mean annual total precipitation	7-10 inches	
Annual evaporation[1] (Lake Wallula)	35 inches	
Mean total snowfall	10-15 inches	
Relative humidity	winter	75-80%
	summer	25-50%
Sunshine (% reaching ground)[2]	winter	25%
	summer	70-85%
Extreme wind velocity	> 80 mph	
Annual thunderstorms	10-15	
[1] dependent on temperature, humidity, and wind velocity [2] measure of cloudiness		

blows eastward over the Coast Ranges, Cascades and/or Rockies, and temporarily the interior basins, such as the Columbia Plateau and/or the Great Plains. Warm, moist air from over the Pacific Ocean cools and causes precipitation as it rises over the west flanks of a mountain range. The now drier air warms as it descends the east side of the mountains. Arid as it is, Wallula Gap doesn't get much snow. However, there can be half a foot of snow on the ground, with a 20 degrees Fahrenheit temperature at sunset. If a chinook comes, by midnight it can be 50 degrees Fahrenheit, and most of the snow disappears. Chinooks in the Wallula area are often from southeasterly winds blowing over the nearby Blue Mountains.

Soils

What is a soil? To a farmer, a soil is where crops grow. To a civil engineer, it doesn't require blasting for removal. To a soil scientist, it is a result of weathering of rock and sediment, and its character is determined by five factors: parent material, climate, topography, organisms and time.

The soils and climate of southeastern Washington and northeastern Oregon are ideal for growing almost anything, especially with a little irrigation. The area is famous for grapes, orchards, onions, potatoes, wheat and alfalfa. Consider part of the label on bottles of Reininger wine: "Cataclysmic geological events, including enormous basaltic lava flows, and fine-grained deposits by the Earth's largest floods have contributed to the superb grape-growing soils of the Walla Walla Valley that help produce award-winning vintages."

The **parent material** at Wallula Gap is mostly basaltic

bedrock overlain by a variable thickness of loess, or windblown silt. Parent materials may also include colluvium, alluvium, Mazama ash and dune sand (see chapter 3). The **climate** is uniform in the Wallula area; it's dry everywhere, and temperatures don't vary much from top to bottom with only about a thousand feet of relief.

The **topography** factor includes relief, slope, aspect (direction the slope faces) and drainage. The steepest slopes are the basalt cliffs of Wallula Gap and side canyons. Also steep are taluses of large, loose rocks and canyon slopes where the basalt bedrock is close to the surface. The uplands at Wallula Gap are dominated by loess soils with gentle slopes and good drainage.

Consider just these three soil-forming factors and the resulting variety of soils at Wallula Gap. The basalt cliffs are too steep for soils to form. The aridity of the area and the extreme permeability of basalt blocks prevent soils from forming on the taluses. The gentle upland slopes with silt-sized loess result in soils that are good for growing wheat. The silt retains moisture, allowing for weathering of the mineral grains. Caliche (calcium carbonate), clay minerals and organic matter slowly accumulate in the soil.

The soil-forming factors interact. Consider the four vegetation associations at Juniper Canyon. The basalt cliffs have no vegetation except lichens and mosses. The south side of the canyon has thick, sandy soils (the prevailing southwesterly winds have transported sand from the Umatilla Basin) and some moisture (despite the permeable sand) because this *north-facing* slope gets less sun. A variety of shrubs, wildflowers and grasses (and even a few juniper trees) grow on the south side. In contrast, the north side has thin, silty soils over the basalt bedrock and little moisture because its *south-facing* slope gets lots of sun; the dominant vegetation is

grass. With a tiny creek and beaver dams, the canyon bottom has considerable moisture despite the low precipitation of the area. The flat, poorly drained canyon floor hosts many species of wetland vegetation, including willows and cattails.

Not only do other soil-forming factors determine the number and types of **organisms**, the plants and animals and even

SOIL SUMMARY: general characteristics of soils at Wallula Gap		
(in part from the soil survey manuals of Benton and Walla Walla counties, Washington, and Umatilla County, Oregon)		
Sides of Wallula Gap	**Factor**	**Uplands near Wallula Gap**
basalt bedrock or rubble (minor sand and silt)	**parent material**	loess (eolian silt)
arid	**climate**	arid
steep	**slope**	gentle
excessive	**drainage**	good
dry	**moisture content**	moderate
little	**natural vegetation**	bunchgrass
little	**current vegetation**	wheat
< 13,000 years	**age of soil**	silt has accumulated for almost 2 million years
grazing, habitat	**land use**	farming, grazing
little to none	**calcium carbonate**	present at depth
none to shallow	**soil depth**	deep
"basalt rock outcrop"	**example of name**	Ritzville silt loam

single-celled bacteria influence the soils. The plants anchor the soil, reducing erosion by water and wind. The plants provide organic matter and shade. Mosses and lichens help to break down rocks. Animal excrement and bacteria fix carbon and add nutrients like nitrogen. Rodents and earthworms till the soil.

Bacteria, lichens, mosses, algae and fungi form cryptobiotic soils or crusts, common in the Wallula area. Also called biological soil crusts, they help to retain moisture, protect native species and keep out exotic species. Once the crust of the cryptobiotic soil is broken by tire, hoof or boot, erosion increases.

The fifth soil-forming factor is **time**. The high places escaped the Missoula floods, so loess has been accumulating on the uplands for almost 2 million years, allowing lots of time for rich soils to form. Wallula Gap itself was cleaned out repeatedly as the Missoula floods roared through between 15,000 and 13,000 years ago. All loose material (from rocks to fine sediment) was removed in most areas, and gravel bars were deposited in a few side canyons; the clock was reset in terms of soil formation. The clock was reset again every time a flash flood charged down a side canyon, sweeping the canyon bottom and depositing mud and boulders on the fan at the mouth of the canyon. Before Lake Wallula existed, incipient soils and riparian vegetation on the Columbia River's floodplain were altered by spring

Juniper Canyon from the west side of Wallula Gap. Note sparseness of vegetation on dark basalt cliffs, grasses on left (south-facing) slope, shrubs and scattered trees on sandy right (north-facing) slope, and dense vegetation in the wetland on the canyon floor. (Bob Carson photo)

Incipient soils at Wallula Gap are developed on transported sediment and the basalt bedrock. Here gravels deposited by the Missoula floods are overlain by reworked wind-deposited silt. (Bob Carson photo)

Contrast the dark basalt of the Twin Sisters with the light sand of the dunes. In late spring sand dock thrives in the sand. Parent material here includes the basalt bedrock, the cone of colluvium at the base of the buttes, and the dune sand. (Bob Carson photo)

Apple orchard at Wallula. (Kathryn Farrell photo)

floods (as much as five times the mean annual discharge of the river).

•••

The geography of the Wallula area is a function of its geologic history, as well as the climate. There were floods of Miocene lava, floods from the failure of Pleistocene ice dams, and Holocene floods from rain and melting snow. Earth materials, climate, weathering and erosion, and plants and animals constantly interact. Floods come and go, soils form and are eroded, and wildlife is in tune with the seasons. The geography of the Wallula area is also influenced by humans who hunt and gather and recreate, and who build structures, from little homes to big dams.

McNary Dam raises the Columbia River about 85 feet, forming a reservoir which extends 64 miles upriver through Wallula Gap to above the Tri-Cities. (Bob Carson photo)

Where the future meets the past: Wind turbines on the Palouse Hills. (Drypoint etching with watercolor and ink by Sandra Rokoff-Lizut)

Bibliography

Quote

Charles Wilkes, 1845, *Narrative of the United States Exploring Expedition during the years 1838, 1839, 1840, 1841, 1842*: London, Wiley and Putnam, v. IV, p. 390.

Soils

Belknap, Jayne and O.L. Lange, eds., 2001, *Biological soil crusts: Structure, function, and management* (Ecological Studies 150): New York, Springer-Verlag, 503 p.

Harrison, E.T., N.C. Donaldson, F.R. McCreary and A.O. Ness, 1957, *Soil survey of Walla Walla County, Washington*: U.S. Department of Agriculture, Soil Conservation Service, 138 p.

Johnson, D.R., and A.J. Makinson, 1988, *Soil survey of Umatilla County area, Oregon*: U.S. Department of Agriculture, Soil Conservation Service, 388 p.

Rassmussen, J.J., 1971, *Soil survey, Benton County area, Washington*: U.S. Department of Agriculture, Soil Conservation Service, 72 p.

Weather and Climate

Mote, P.W., 2003, "Trends in temperature and precipitation in the Pacific Northwest during the twentieth century": *Northwest Science*, v. 77, no. 4, p. 271-282

Nelson, E.R., 1949, "Columbia River Basin Flood, May-June 1948": *Monthly Weather Review*, v. 77, no. 1, 10 p.

Phillips, E.L., 1970, *Washington climate for these counties, Asotin, Benton, Columbia, Franklin, Garfield, Walla Walla*: Pullman, Washington, Washington State University, 93 p.

Taylor, G.H., and Chris Hannan, 1999, *The climate of Oregon: From rain forest to desert*: Corvallis, Oregon, Oregon State University Press, 211 p.

Taylor, G.H., and R.R. Hatton, 1999, *The Oregon weather book: A state of extremes*: Corvallis, Oregon, Oregon State University Press, 242 p.

An iceberg carried this granitic erratic to the top of the Horse Heaven Hills on the west side of Wallula Gap. The Blue Mountains anticline is in the distance. (John Clement photo)

3

Geology:
Fire and Flood Along the Columbia

Robert J. Carson

"Rivers reflect a continent's history. Where forces far beneath the Earth's crust force up
mountain ranges, rivers flow swift and cold down steep, boulder-strewn channels. Where the
Earth is still, rivers meander broadly, depositing thick plains of sand, silt, and clay."

–Ellen Wohl, *Disconnected Rivers*, 2004

The next time you're at Wallula Gap, look at the high cliffs on the northwest side. If you're in a boat on Lake Wallula, look west from where the reservoir orientation switches from north-south to northeast-southwest. If you're on U.S. Highway 730, stop at Port Kelley and look northwest, or pull in at the Twin Sisters (Two Sisters) and look southwest. Locate the highest point on the cliffs, where there is a bench mark appropriately named Bluff, at an elevation of 1,147 feet, 807 feet above the normal pool elevation of Lake Wallula. Geologist or not, if you were up there, you would see some truly phenomenal evidence of Wallula Gap's history going back about 15 million years.

High bluffs on the west side of Wallula Gap. The uppermost lava flow on the left is only about half as old as all the other lava flows; it was emplaced at about the level of Lake Wallula and uplifted hundreds of feet in millions of years. (Bob Carson photo)

Before we go up there to the Bluff bench mark, let's look around. First, all the bedrock in every direction is basalt, lava flows from a time when the climate was warmer and wetter than today. Second, note that most of the lava flows have a lower portion – the colonnade – of large polygonal columns, and an upper portion – or entablature – of much smaller and less regular columns. Third, note that you don't see much sediment except for some windblown sand or silt; the Columbia River gravels are drowned beneath about 40 feet of reservoir water. Fourth, you don't see any glaciers or icebergs; the nearest glaciers are 120 miles west on Mount Adams, and as for icebergs, well, maybe in Alaska.

If you were to walk to the Bluff bench mark along the northwest rim of Wallula Gap, you would find at elevations as high as 1,120 feet granite boulders weighing as much as 5 tons from the general vicinity of northern Idaho. A glacier didn't carry them here, because the big ice sheet from British Columbia stopped about 125 miles north of here near Grand Coulee Dam. Icebergs rafted the granite here, riding floods more than 800 feet deep from ice-dammed Glacial Lake Missoula in Montana. The last series of these catastrophic deluges started about 15,000 years ago, with floods occurring every decade or so for two millennia. The minimum size of an iceberg that can float a 5-ton rock is about 11 feet in each dimension. At least one of the erratic rocks near Bluff has striations proving that a glacier dragged it over bedrock – somewhere far to the north – before an iceberg carried it here.

What about the bedrock up at Bluff? The very summit is the base of a lava flow, a colonnade of basalt columns 3 feet to 6 feet in diameter. Beneath the colonnade sits about 10 feet of sediment. The bottom of this sediment is indurated sand; the top is multicolored pebbles and cobbles, rounded and mostly disc-shaped. The stones resemble beach pebbles and cobbles, but the ocean is much farther away than the river below. The stones are not basaltic; they are volcanic rocks from near Challis, Idaho, and quartzites from 1 billion-year-old rocks in western Montana. Their rock types don't match the Columbia River sediments at the bottom of the reservoir. Was a river here? What river? Why are river sediments up here?

Beneath the sand, pebbles and cobbles is the top of an older lava flow, an entablature of basalt columns less than a foot in diameter. Geologists have been studying the basalt flows (and interbeds of sediment) of eastern Washington and Oregon for decades. All the lava flows below the stones at Bluff are 14 million to 15 million years old, erupted in a subsiding basin. Concurrent with the eruptions and the subsidence was the deformation causing the Yakima Fold Belt. The easternmost fold is along the Horse Heaven Hills Anticline; the southwest-flowing river crossed that east-west anticlinal ridge here at the lowest place. The channel was cut into the old lava flows and filled with sand, pebbles and cobbles. Based on the lithologies (quartzite from Montana, volcanic rocks from Idaho), we know that the river was the ancestral Clearwater-Salmon River, not the modern Snake or Columbia River. Then about 8.5 million years ago, lava flowed down and filled the valley, forcing the river to cut a new channel nearby.

Large, granitic boulder resting at an elevation of 1,120 feet on the west rim of Wallula Gap. The iceberg transporting this rock was riding a Missoula flood about 800 feet above the Columbia River. In the distance is the delta of the Walla Walla River. (Mike Denny photo)

Gravel of the ancestral Clearwater-Salmon River. These pebbles and cobbles, mostly Precambrian quartzite from Idaho or Montana, are buried beneath an 8.5 million-year-old basalt flow atop the western side of Wallula Gap. (Bob Carson photo)

The ancestral Clearwater-Salmon River cut Wallula Gap across the Horse Heaven Hills. The Columbia River shifted eastward to join the Clearwater-Salmon River at the gap. Still later, the Salmon River captured the Snake River, and Hells Canyon was born.

During the relatively recent Ice Age, the water of each giant flood from Montana's Glacial Lake Missoula could not get through narrow Wallula Gap all at once. The water backed up and rose high enough to spill over the edges of the gap. Icebergs carrying granitic boulders got stranded on the shore, more than 800 feet above the river's normal height of about 300 feet.

The final chapter of ups and downs at Wallula Gap was another inundation that occurred only decades ago. The water rose, not due to floods from the northeast, but because of McNary Dam to the southwest.

Millions of years ago, basalt flows buried and burned whatever life was present here. Thousands of years ago, glacial floods drowned the animals and uprooted the plants at Wallula Gap. In this chapter we will examine the geologic history of the Wallula area.

Geologic Time Scale for Wallula Gap

A.D. 1953   McNary Dam drowns the floor of Wallula Gap.

Years Ago

7,700   Mazama ash from the eruption that produced Crater Lake in southwestern Oregon falls on the Horse Heaven Hills.

12,000   Beginning of the Holocene Epoch of the Quaternary Period. Approximate time of extinction of large mammals.

12,700?   Last Missoula flood of the late Pleistocene flood episode.

13,000   Mount St. Helens ash falls on one of the Touchet Beds.

14,300   Approximate time of arrival of American Indians.

15,300?   First Missoula flood of the late Pleistocene flood episode. Touchet Beds begin to be deposited.

20,000   Peak of last glaciation. Sea level 400 feet below present. Very cold at Wallula Gap.

125,000   Peak of last interglaciation. Climate at Wallula Gap similar to today's.

780,000   Earth's magnetic field switches from reversed to normal polarity.

1 million?   Early Missoula flood episode.

1.6 million Beginning of the Pleistocene Epoch of the Quaternary Period. Loess deposition begins on the Horse Heaven Hills.

3 million?   Snake River captured by the Salmon River, cuts Hells Canyon and flows to the Pasco Basin.

4 million? Columbia River shifts eastward to join the Clearwater-Salmon River and flows through Wallula Gap.

5.3 million Beginning of the Pliocene Epoch of the Tertiary Period. Ringold Formation deposited before and after this date.

8.5 million Eruption of Martindale flow of the Ice Harbor Member of the Saddle Mountains Basalt.

10.5 million Eruption of the Elephant Mountain flow of the Saddle Mountains Basalt.

12 million Eruption of the Pomona flow of the Saddle Mountains Basalt.

14 million Eruption of two lava flows of the Umatilla Member of the Saddle Mountains Basalt.

15.3 million Eruption of eight to 10 lava flows of the Frenchman Springs Member of the Wanapum Basalt.

15.6 million Eruption of the last lava flows of the Grande Ronde Basalt. Five Grande Ronde flows with normal polarity are exposed at Wallula Gap.

16.5 million Eruption of the first lava flows of the Grande Ronde Basalt (well below water level at Wallula Gap).

17 million Eruption of the oldest lavas (Imnaha Basalt) of the Columbia River Basalt Group in the Hells Canyon area, and of lava flows (Steens Basalt) in southeastern Oregon. The growth of anticlines of the Yakima Fold Belt and the subsidence of basins begin and probably continue today.

23.8 million Beginning of the Miocene Epoch of the Tertiary Period.

50 million? Early Tertiary sediments and volcanics emplaced. May be present beneath the basalt flows at Wallula Gap.

65 million Dinosaurs become extinct. Beginning of the Tertiary Period of the Cenozoic Era.

100 million? Granitic plutons emplaced as exotic terranes collide with North America. This granite may be present under the lava flows at Wallula Gap.

248 million Beginning of the Mesozoic Era. For about 100 million years, volcanic and sedimentary rocks form far to the southwest. They drift toward the Pacific Northwest and may underlie the basalt flows at Wallula Gap.

543 million Beginning of the Paleozoic Era. Until now most life is marine, unicellular, soft-bodied and unlikely to be preserved as fossils.

4.6 billion Origin of solar system, including the Earth. Meteorites are this old. Beginning of Precambrian Era.

Basaltic Lava Flows

Most of the rock and sediment at Wallula Gap originated elsewhere. There is no granitic bedrock exposed as in Oregon's Wallowa Mountains or at Washington's Snoqualmie Pass, where huge masses of magma were intruded into the Earth's crust. No volcanoes erupted here, as they have in the Cascade Range. There is no exposed metamorphic bedrock, heated and squeezed from other rocks for millions of years. There is no limestone left from some ancient reef.

Most of the earth materials at Wallula Gap were on their way to somewhere else. The bedrock here is all basalt, the "frozen" remnant of lava rivers and lava lakes; the lava erupted to the east, perhaps where Hells Canyon is today, and flowed west, at times as far as the Pacific Ocean. The only other volcanic material here is ash from the eruption of Mount Mazama; perhaps an inch of white ash fell from the clouds that scurried from southwestern Oregon to Alberta, surprising American Indians throughout the Pacific Northwest. For almost 2 million years, the wind has transported silt-sized particles from one place to another in eastern Washington and Oregon. The prevailing winds blow these dust clouds generally toward the northeast; some of the silt settles at Wallula Gap. What may have been the world's greatest floods swept from Montana to the Pacific. The muddy water held enormous amounts of sediment, and giant, dirty icebergs rode the waves. Some sediment was deposited in giant gravel bars high on the sides of Wallula Gap; even higher, receding floodwaters stranded icebergs.

The bedrock and sediment at Wallula Gap record only the last one-third of 1 percent of the Earth's 4.6 billion years of existence. And that history is incomplete; millions of years are unrecorded. This canyon is no Grand Canyon with rocks spanning 2 billion years, not even a Hells Canyon with rocks representing 300 million years of Earth's history. At Wallula Gap the bedrock is less than 17 million years old.

As stated before, the bedrock at Wallula Gap is all basalt. Why are these lava flows here? How old are they? Where did they come from? What is under the basalt? Why is the basalt pushed up into a ridge? Why does the Columbia River cross the Horse Heaven Hills here? How long has this river been at Wallula Gap? Geologists know the answers to some of these questions and theorize about others. The story of the basalt begins about 300 miles to the south.

About 17 million years ago, volcanism began just west of where Oregon, Idaho and Nevada join. The volcanism started at a "hot spot," likely where a mantle plume encountered the Earth's crust. A mantle plume is a buoyant body of magma that may rise 2,000 miles from the boundary between the Earth's core and mantle. When the plume encounters the crust, it may cause two main types of eruptions. The magma may penetrate the crust with relatively little modification and cause basaltic eruptions. The basaltic eruptions are generally quiet lava flows (similar to typical Hawaiian eruptions), but there may be local explosive volcanism (such as the cinder cones at Craters of the Moon National Monument in Idaho). The other option for the mantle plume is to melt the base of the earth's crust to produce rhyolitic magma. Rhyolitic eruptions are typically explosive, with lots of ash and pumice, but they may be quiet and result in obsidian flows (as with Newberry Volcano in central Oregon).

The hot spot volcanism apparently migrated in at least three directions from McDermitt Volcano in northernmost Nevada: northeast, north and northwest. Let us consider the northeast route first, the route that leads 400 miles along the Snake River Plain to Yellowstone National Park. This northeasterly migration is in the opposite direction of North America's movement. Geological and geophysical evidence, plus actual surveying using satellites, indicate that the North American plate is moving southwesterly. Therefore, what appears to be northeasterly migration of hot spot volcanism from Nevada to northwestern Wyoming may actually be North

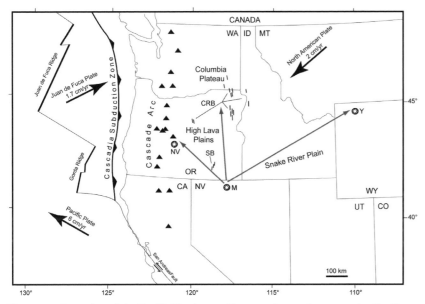

Plate tectonic setting of the Pacific Northwest. Between the northwest-moving Pacific Plate and the southwest-moving North American Plate, the small Juan de Fuca Plate is being subducted eastward, resulting in the volcanoes of the Cascade Range. Farther east, a mantle plume originated at the McDermott volcanic field (M) about 17 million years ago. Volcanism progressed rapidly northward, erupting through dikes (vertical bars) in southeastern Oregon at Steens Mountain (the Steens Basalt, SB) and in northeastern Oregon and adjacent states (the Columbia River basalts, CRB). Volcanism progressed slowly from the McDermott volcanic field northeasterly across Idaho's Snake River Plain to Yellowstone (Y) and northwesterly across Oregon's High Lava Plains to Newberry Volcano (NV). (After Jordan et al., 2004)

America moving southwest over a mantle plume fixed in position. This theory is not perfect because the rate of migration of hot spot volcanism (4 centimeters per year) is about twice as fast as the drift of North America (2 centimeters per year). However, the hot spot has, in fact, migrated to Yellowstone and left the Snake River Plain in its wake. At the surface, the Snake River Plain is mostly basalt, but beneath there is mostly rhyolite. In the Yellowstone area, most of the young rock is rhyolite that erupted explosively, but there are some basaltic lava flows.

Next, consider the line of volcanism that runs 200 miles northwest from McDermitt Volcano. These basaltic and rhyolitic volcanic centers are about 16 million years old in southeastern Oregon and younger toward the northwest, where eruptions have occurred at Newberry Volcano in central Oregon within the past 2,000 years. Of the lines of volcanism that radiate from southeastern Oregon, this northwest trend erupted the lowest volume of magma. Newberry Volcano is a huge shield volcano with a big caldera (giant crater) such as Hawaii's Mauna Loa. Eruptions at the Hawaiian hot spot are almost entirely basalt, whereas Newberry Volcano has erupted basalt, andesite and rhyolite. Newberry Volcano may be related to the Cascade Range volcanism; for example, in the nearby Three Sisters area, near Newberry in the Cascades, there are flows of basalt, andesite, and rhyolite. Andesite (named for the Andes) has properties intermediate between those of basalt and rhyolite.

But what about the volcanic rocks at Wallula Gap? The northern arm of volcanism formed the basalt flows at Wallula Gap. It differs from the other arms in the following respects:

1. Here was the greatest volume of magma in the shortest amount of time.

2. Here the magma was almost all basaltic, with little explosive volcanism. (A possible exception is the Powder River volcanics in northeastern Oregon.)

3. The volcanism did not continue into the Ice Age (the last 2 million years); rather, the last eruption on the northern arm was 6 million years ago. (Again, the Powder River volcanics are an exception, with the last eruption about 2 million years ago near Elgin, Oregon.)

4. The volcanism on this arm may have all begun at about the same time. From Steens Mountain in southeastern Oregon to eastern Washington's Columbia Plateau, the basaltic eruptions may have all started about 17 million years ago.

These basalt flows that erupted from 17 million to 6 million years ago are called the Columbia River Basalt Group, or the Columbia River basalts. The basaltic magmas had temperatures in the range of 1,700 to 2,200 degrees Fahrenheit. The more than 300 individual lava flows are separated into five or more formations, depending on what geologist does the division. Three of these formations are present at Wallula Gap; from oldest to youngest, they are the Grande Ronde Basalt, the Wanapum Basalt and the Saddle Mountains Basalt. Geologic formations are named for geographic places where particular rocks were first described and/ or are best exposed. The Columbia River flows across a lot of basalt. The Grande Ronde Basalt is named for exposures along the lower Grande Ronde River near its confluence with the Snake River in southeastern Washington. The Saddle Mountains are a long ridge at the north edge of the Pasco Basin. Wanapum Dam lies along the Columbia River just north of the Saddle Mountains. (The Touchet

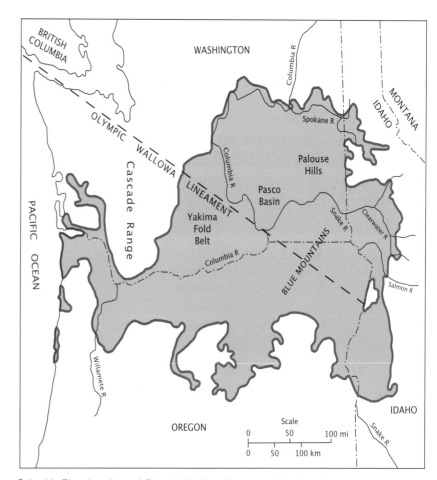

Columbia River basalts and Olympic-Wallowa lineament. The lava flows of the Columbia River basalts erupted from vents in northeastern Oregon and adjacent Washington and Idaho. Although some lava flowed east and south, most went north to the general vicinity of the Spokane River and west to the Cascade Range. Some flows followed ancient courses of the Columbia River toward the Pacific coast, getting as far north as Grays Harbor, Washington and as far south as Yaquina Head, Oregon. E.J. Raisz proposed that the Olympic-Wallowa lineament (OWL) extended from the Strait of Juan de Fuca between the Olympic Mountains and Vancouver Island to the northern flank of the Wallowa Mountains in northeastern Oregon. The OWL is a young fault from near Wallula Gap to the eastern side of the Cascade Range. (After Tolan and Reidel, 1989)

Beds, covered later in this chapter, are named for exposures along the Walla Walla River south of the town of Touchet.) The total volume of the Columbia River basalts is more than 40,000 cubic miles; they cover about 64,000 square miles of Washington, Oregon and western Idaho. The Columbia River basalts are particularly thick – two miles – in the Pasco Basin; their top is 200 feet below sea level. The lava flows were erupted from dikes, some near Wallula, most farther east. Dikes are fissures along which magma travels, crosscutting pre-existing rocks. Many dikes are exposed along the Snake and Grande Ronde rivers and in the Wallowa Mountains of northeastern Oregon.

The Columbia River basalt feeder dikes, near vertical and trending north-south, are in vent systems as much as 100 miles long. From these vents the basalt flowed only a short distance southeast because that direction was uphill. Most of the magma flowed downhill, north as far as the Okanogan Highlands of northern Washington, and west to the ancestral Cascades. Some of the flows made it all the way down the ancestral Columbia River to the Pacific Ocean. The Pomona flow, which erupted from a fissure in western Idaho 12 million years ago, has a volume of about 170 cubic miles; this flow, present at Wallula Gap, went more than 350 miles from its vent to the Pacific Ocean.

Theories differ about how fast these flows may have traveled. One model specifies a lava flow with a front 50 miles wide and 100 feet tall, moving westward at two to three miles an hour. However, such a flow would cool to solid lava if it took more than days or weeks to get across Washington. Another model indicates that the flows were fed internally, with the flows growing thicker from inflation. The magma would have been well insulated, allowing a flow to take years to get from its vent to the coast.

What rocks lie beneath the mile or two of basalts at Wallula Gap? The oldest candidate, an exotic terrane, is a diverse suite of igneous, sedimentary and metamorphic rocks about 200 million years old; part of an island arc like the Marianas Islands, they drifted north and east from near the equator and slammed into North America about 100 million years ago (at that time, the west edge of North America was near the western border of Idaho). The next oldest possibility is 100-million-year-old granitic rock, formed during the collision just mentioned, that makes up the core of the Wallowa Mountains. The youngest candidate, Early Tertiary in age, about 50 million years old, is volcanic and sedimentary rocks

Left: A black basalt dike cuts the granitic face of Eagle Cap near the center of Oregon's Wallowa Mountains. **Right:** This basalt dike in Hells Canyon of the Snake River may have fed a lava flow at Wallula Gap. (Bob Carson photos)

widespread in central Oregon and in the Cascades.

All three of these possible candidates crop out beneath the Columbia River basalts only 45 miles south of Wallula Gap. The rocks are exposed south of Pilot Rock, Oregon, in the vicinity of Birch Creek and Battle Mountain Summit. The exotic terrane rocks are also exposed 60 miles east of Wallula Gap along the Tucannon River in the Blue Mountains. An exploratory oil and gas well encountered metamorphic rocks about a mile and a half beneath the surface in northwestern Walla Walla County. The granitic rocks crop out 80 miles to the northeast at Lower Granite Dam on the Snake River. Another well searching for petroleum found noncommercial gas in Early Tertiary rocks 80 miles northwest of Wallula Gap; the

well penetrated about three miles of Columbia River basalts in Yakima Canyon between Ellensburg and Yakima. Any or all of these rocks – exotic terrane, granitic or Early Tertiary – could lie beneath the big pile of basalt flows at Wallula Gap.

There are about 19 lava flows exposed in the sides of Wallula Gap, each with an average thickness of 50 feet. From the crest of the Horse Heaven Hills, the flows dip gently north toward the Pasco Basin and south toward the Umatilla Basin. This dip is a result of the uplift of the Horse Heaven Hills; the original dip of the flows was westward toward the coast, away from the rising mountains

This cliff reveals approximately half of the 19 Miocene basalt flows exposed at Wallula Gap. (Bob Carson photo)

The Twin Sisters are buttes or scabs carved by the Missoula floods. They are composed of a single lava flow; the basal colonnade has much larger columns (good for rock climbing) than the upper entablature. (Dianne Kornberg photo)

of northeastern Oregon. All of these dips are so gentle (only a few degrees) that the lava flows are nearly horizontal.

As each lava flow cooled, it contracted with vertical joints forming. Just as the shrinking of drying mud results in a polygonal pattern, so does the cooling of lava to rock. The joints separate polygonal columns with four, five, six or seven sides. Most Columbia River basalt flows have a lower colonnade and an upper entablature (architectural terms). The colonnade is generally thinner, but may be almost nonexistent to dominant (leaving most to very little of the flow for the entablature). The colonnade is so named because the columns are larger, straighter and more regular, resulting from slow cooling upward from the base of the flow where heat is escaping downward.

In contrast, the smaller, less-regular columns of the entablature, found above the colonnade, may be chaotic or bent. Above the entablature may be flow-top breccia, consisting of sharp fragments embedded in a fine-grained matrix, formed as the chilled crust repeatedly breaks as it is carried along on the moving molten interior of the lava flow. The size of the columns is a measure of the rate of cooling – the slower the heat loss, the larger the columns. Consider the huge columns at Devils Tower in northeastern Wyoming; this rock cooled very slowly because it was subvolcanic (below the ground) and, therefore, well-insulated. There is a range of thickness of the individual lava flows at Wallula Gap: the thicker the flow, the slower the cooling.

Geologists are unsure as to the reasons for the dramatic difference between colonnade and entablature. Surface water would hasten the cooling of the entablature. We know that the climate was wet when these flows erupted, so rain fell on top of the flows.

Also, the lava flows dammed streams, with the result that lakes likely flooded the flow surfaces.

Why was this dry area at Wallula Gap wet 15 million years ago? There are two reasons for the extra moisture then: a wetter climate (see below) and interactions between lava and rivers. The Columbia, Clearwater, Salmon and most likely the Snake River all came together in this area between the Rockies and the Cascades. With every eruption, the dense lava obeyed the law of gravity and went to the lowest place, a river channel. The lava blocked the river, creating a lake. As more lava came out of the fissure, part of it went into the lake. Lava cooling underwater does not form a colonnade and an entablature; it forms what is called pillow lava or pillow basalt – huge pillow-shaped masses of basalt piled on top of each other. The rims of the pillows are black volcanic glass due to the quenching of the outside of the pillow by the water. The insides of the pillows may contain radiating columnar joints due to cooling and contraction. Hot magma entering cold water results in explosions (and pillow implosions) that may fragment part or all of the lava; between the pillows may be orange palagonite – fragments altered by reaction with the water. Pillow basalt is exposed in a road cut at the north end of Wallula Gap (see appendix 1: Road Log, mile 13.9).

The time between the individual emplacement of flows ranges from years to millions of years. Between the flows there may be quite a variety of materials:

1. Lake deposits: fine-grained sediments, in places (e.g., Grant County, Washington) with diatomite from diatom (a single-celled organism with a siliceous "test" or shell) blooms in the lakes.

2. Marsh deposits: peat turned to low-grade coal (e.g., Asotin County, Washington).
3. Stream deposits: sand and gravel (e.g., beneath the Lower Monumental basalt flow just south of Lower Monumental Dam on the Snake River).
4. Ash: from the Snake River Plain and perhaps the ancestral Cascades.
5. Lateritic soil: red soils rich in oxides and hydroxides of iron and aluminum. Laterites form in tropical and subtropical wet climates in places like Brazil and Costa Rica. Lateritic soil between some Columbia River basalt flows

means that the climate then was warmer and moister than today's. The ancestral Cascade Range was not as high as the modern Cascades, so more moisture penetrated the interior. In addition, the Earth's climate was warmer 15 million years ago. That there was a warm, moist climate when the Columbia River basalts erupted is substantiated by the associated fossils. For example, the petrified trees at Gingko Petrified Forest State Park at Vantage, Washington, are subtropical species.

Experts on the Columbia River basalts – geologists Don Swanson, Tom Wright, Steve Reidel, Terry Tolan and Peter Hooper –

Left: Pillow basalt formed as a lava flow entered water. The rinds of the pillows are glassy due to instant cooling as the red-hot lava encountered cold water.
Right: Basaltic breccia at the top of one lava flow overlain by the basal colonnade of the next younger flow. This is a flow-top breccia formed by repeated breaking of quickly cooled crust as the molten interior of the lava continued to flow. (Bob Carson photos)

can distinguish individual lava flows based on several characteristics. One is paleomagnetism: iron-bearing minerals, such as magnetite, record the Earth's magnetic field as a lava flow cools. Effectively, the rock records the direction and distance to the north magnetic pole; these measurements relate to declination (the angle between true and magnetic north) and inclination (the angle between the Earth's surface and the local magnetic field). Because the Earth's magnetic poles are almost always near the poles of rotation, the inclination of the magnetic field is an approximation of the latitude. Therefore, the magnetic field recorded in a 15 million-year-old lava flow tells the paleolatitude of that eruption. Wallula Gap is at 46 degrees north latitude. If a basalt flow here had a magnetic field with an inclination of 35 degrees north, we would assume it had moved about 11 degrees (760 miles) north. Although we can determine the paleolatitude of many rocks (and how much they have rotated), we cannot tell their paleolongitude.

The Earth's magnetic field shifts constantly. Most of the time the shifts are slow; for example, as the north magnetic pole creeps across Arctic Canada, the declination at Wallula Gap changes 1 degree every decade. Occasionally, however, the Earth's magnetic field reverses; that is, it shifts 180 degrees very quickly, probably in less than a thousand years. It is unclear if the shift is by rotation, or by turning off, then turning on in the opposite direction. If the latter, solar radiation would dramatically increase (the magnetic field shields life on Earth from most harmful radiation). The time interval between reversals of the Earth's magnetic field is extremely variable. For example, about 1 million years ago, the field reversed from normal to reversed and back again within about 100,000 years. "Normal" means current conditions, with the north-seeking

end of a compass needle pointing to the north magnetic pole. If the magnetic field were suddenly to reverse right now, you would see a compass needle rotate 180 degrees. At various times in the geologic past, based on current evidence, reversals did not occur for millions of years. The last reversal, from reversed polarity to normal, occurred 780,000 years ago.

Their magnetic polarity provides one of the chief methods of identifying the many lava flows of the Grande Ronde Basalt. Eighty-five percent of the total volume of the Columbia River basalts is in the Grande Ronde Basalt. During the short time of these eruptions (16.5 million to 15.6 million years ago), the earth's magnetic field reversed three times. The earliest Grande Ronde flows (R_1) are reversed; the subsequent flows are called N_1, R_2 and N_2, based on their magnetic polarity. Only the youngest Grande Ronde flows (N_2) with normal polarity are found at Wallula Gap.

Another way to distinguish Columbia River basalt flows is by their mineralogy. All the flows have about the same amounts of the dominant minerals plagioclase feldspar and pyroxene. For the most part these minerals are microscopic and mixed with volcanic glass because the flows cooled quickly. However, some flows have large – up to fingernail size – crystals called phenocrysts. It is uncertain as to whether the most common phenocrysts, plagioclase, grew in the magma chamber before the eruption, and/or in thick lava flows as they slowly cooled. Beside phenocrysts, other small features in the dark lava flows include vesicles and amygdules. Vesicles, or volcanic gas bubble cavities, are most common near the tops of flows. Amygdules, or filled vesicles, may contain quartz, opal, calcite or one of a family of minerals called zeolites.

A third way to distinguish lava flows is by their chemistry;

A. Massive basalt with just a few tiny vesicles (gas bubble cavities). The lighter surface is somewhat weathered compared to the fresh, black surface. **B.** Vesicular basalt. The dark circles and ovals are shadows in vesicles. **C.** Amygdaloidal basalt. The vesicles that formed as the lava cooled were later partly or completely filled with mineral matter to become amygdules. (Bob Carson photos)

this requires a chemical analysis, so it is not a typical field technique. The Columbia River basalts are composed mostly of the oxides of silicon, aluminum, iron, calcium, magnesium, sodium and potassium (in that order of abundance). There is not a lot of variation in the abundance of these major elements. There are exceptions: For example, the Pomona flow, which was very large and traveled very far, has an abnormally high magnesium content and a very low potassium content. Most of the volume of the Columbia River "basalts" has a silicon dioxide content greater than 52 percent, so technically they are basaltic andesites; the range is from about 49 percent to 57 percent. In contrast to the general rule of little variation in major element abundance, there is quite a range of values for trace elements, so this is a good way to track individual lava flows across the Columbia Plateau. For example, the variation in zirconium oxide ranges from 50 parts per million to 200 parts per million.

To summarize the geology so far stated, hundreds of basalt flows were erupted, generally to the east and south of Wallula Gap. As the lava flowed west and north, it disrupted existing drainage. About 19 of these basalt flows are exposed in the sides of the water gap where the Columbia River currently crosses the ridge of the Horse Heaven Hills.

Faults and Folds

The ridge that extends east and west from Wallula Gap is the result of the growth of a faulted anticline. Faults and anticlines are structures caused by breaking and bending, respectively. Faults break and displace rocks and are associated with earthquakes.

Anticlines are long, narrow upfolds of rocks. Folding usually results in downwarps, synclines or basins between the anticlines, such as the Pasco Basin just north of the Horse Heaven Hills. Another type of structural deformation is tilting; the Columbia River basalts tilt gently downward from Spokane to the Pasco Basin. Such structures grew during the eruption of the Columbia River basalts. For millions of years the area east of Wallula Gap has been rising, resulting in a tilt to the west that directed the basalt flows toward the Cascade Range. For millions of years the Pasco Basin has been subsiding, which accounts for the great thickness of basalt flows there. East-west extension allowed the fissures to open and spew forth the lava flows.

North-south compression of the area caused the lava flows to wrinkle into east-west trending anticlines and synclines called the Yakima Fold Belt. The cities of Yakima and Ellensburg are in synclines. If you take Interstate 82 between these two cities, you cross three anticlines. All but one of the many folds in the Yakima area die out going eastward. Only the Horse Heaven Hills Anticline extends all the way east to the Blue Mountains. As we will see, this anticline is important in terms of drainage in the Pacific Northwest. The Blue Mountains themselves are an anticline, oriented northeast-southwest; the Blue Mountains anticline is much larger than the individual anticlines of the Yakima folds.

There is evidence for three major kinds of faults near Wallula Gap. The San Andreas Fault is not, of course, near Wallula Gap, but it has some bearing on the area. The San Andreas Fault is a *strike-slip fault*, in which the motion is parallel to the orientation of the fault. It is the boundary between the northwest-moving Pacific Plate (imagine this as most of the floor of the Pacific Ocean) and

View northwest from the crest of the Horse Heaven Hills anticline. This Arnold Photo from the 1930s shows the basalt flows across the Columbia River dipping north; they descend to beneath sea level in the distant Pasco Basin. In the foreground are basalts eroded by the Missoula floods. The small white objects on the east bank of the river are fuel tanks at Attalia. (Fred L. Mitchell Collection)

Geology: Fire and Flood Along the Columbia　55

Looking west-northwest along the Olympic-Wallowa lineament. The Horse Heaven Hills are up on the left; the eastern Pasco Basin, down on the right. In the distance, the Walla Walla River is building a delta into Lake Wallula. (Bob Carson photo)

the southwest-moving North American Plate (consider this most of North America plus Greenland and the west half of the floor of the North Atlantic Ocean). A similar strike-slip fault, the Queen Charlotte Islands Fault, lies just off the coast of British Columbia. As the Pacific Plate moves northwest, it tries to drag portions of western North America with it. This probably results in northwest-oriented faults like the Brothers Fault Zone that stretches southeast from Bend, Oregon.

Crossing the north end of Wallula Gap is the Olympic-Wallowa lineament (OWL). This lineament, or alignment of topographic features, stretches northwest from the north flank of the Wallowa Mountains in northeastern Oregon to the Strait of Juan de Fuca between Washington's Olympic Mountains and Vancouver Island, British Columbia. From at least Cle Elum on the east side of the Cascades to Milton-Freewater, just east of Wallula Gap, the aligned topographic features are associated with a fault. At least minor strike-slip movement on the Wallula fault zone is substantiated by subhorizontal slickenlines, parallel scratches on the fault surface, near Wallula Junction (see appendix 1: Road Log, mile 14.1).

The second type of fault is *dip-slip*, which means that the motion is perpendicular to the orientation of the fault, and there are two kinds of dip-slip faults. Along the OWL east of Wallula Gap, the topography indicates a steeply dipping *normal fault*: the Horse Heaven Hills have moved up relative to the lower Walla Walla Valley along the Wallula fault zone. The specific landforms here are called faceted or truncated spurs. They appear as small ridges extending north from the main east-west ridge of the Horse Heaven Hills, abruptly ending in steep, triangular areas aligned on the OWL. This interpretation of dip-slip along the OWL does not agree with the strike-slip interpretation based on the slickenlines; however, the fault probably moved dip-slip at times and strike-slip at other times.

The other kind of dip-slip fault is a *low-angle thrust fault*. Imagine the wrinkling of the basalt flows into anticlines and synclines as the Yakima Fold Belt was created during north-south oriented compression. After a while the brittle rocks started sliding over each other along thrust faults. The thrust faults associated with the anticlines cause them to pop up relative to the adjacent synclines as the compression shortens the fold belt.

Most of the structures mentioned were growing during the eruptions of the basalts and may be active yet today. Evidence for growth of the anticlines during volcanic activity is that some of the

Truncated spurs at the base of the Horse Heaven Hills just east of Wallula Gap. This portion of the Olympic-Wallowa lineament is the fault that likely caused the earthquake farther east in 1936. (Bob Carson photo)

lava flows are thinner (or absent) over the crests of the anticlines. The 1936 Milton-Freewater earthquake may indicate that the Wallula fault zone is seismically active.

Rearranging the Rivers

With all the data and evidence regarding lava flows, ancient rivers, folding and faulting, geologists try to synthesize a geologic history for this area. The lava flows just older than the Grande Ronde Basalt are called the Imnaha Basalt (not present at Wallula Gap). These early Imnaha lava flows filled pre-existing valleys. Because of low relief and a gentle slope to the northwest, when the Grande Ronde eruptions occurred east and southeast of Wallula Gap, the lavas flowed over this area, leaving thin (average thickness 50 feet) sheets of basalt. The flows were somewhat like wide lava rivers, and because of partial ponding farther north and west, somewhat like lava lakes. Some of the Grande Ronde flows were voluminous enough to get across or through the Cascades to the Pacific Ocean. Some high places with old rock, like Steptoe Butte in eastern Washington, never were overtopped by all the lava flows.

As stated before, the Grande Ronde flows, which erupted between 16.5 million and 15.6 million years ago, comprise 85 percent of the total volume of the Columbia River basalts. The Columbia River may have earlier been closer to the center of the basin between the Cascades and the Rockies, far from Wallula Gap. The Grande Ronde flows forced the river north against the Okanogan Highlands and west against the Cascades. A temporary lull in the eruptions, perhaps 100,000 years long, allowed lateritic soil to develop on top of the youngest Grande Ronde flows. This soil

Late Cenozoic drainage changes on the Columbia Plateau. (After Fecht et al., 1987)

A. 17 million years ago, before the eruption of the Columbia River basalts. The Columbia River flows southwesterly from British Columbia across the Okanogan Highlands toward a route through the ancestral Cascade Range. The Yakima River is a western tributary from the central Washington Cascades. The Clearwater River takes an unknown route westward from the Northern Rocky Mountains.

B. 15 million years ago, after the eruption of most of the volume of the Columbia River basalts. From vents in northeastern Oregon and adjacent Washington and Idaho, some lava flowed eastward up the valley of the Clearwater River, and southward into central Oregon. Most of the lava flowed northwesterly, pushing the Columbia River north against the Okanogan Highlands and west against the ancestral Cascades. Sedimentation by some large streams such as the Yakima River may have shoved the Columbia River out onto the lava flows.

C. 13 million years ago. The growth of an anticline in the Yakima Fold Belt of central Washington forces the Columbia River eastward away from the margin of the Columbia Plateau. This process was likely helped by deposition of sediment on the eastern flank of the Cascade Range. Coming from central Idaho, the Salmon River has joined the Clearwater River; together they flow west to the Columbia.

D. 11 million years ago, after almost all of the flows of Columbia River basalt have erupted. The ancestral Clearwater-Salmon River has shifted south to Wallula Gap where it is joined by the Walla Walla and Umatilla Rivers; from there it flows west more or less along the Oregon-Washington state line.

E. 5 million years ago. The last of the Columbia River basalts, the Lower Monumental flow, erupted 6 million years ago. Both the Columbia River and the Yakima River have shifted east to the Pasco Basin. In part, this was due to the buildup of sediments shed from the Cascade Range. The growth of the Horse Heaven Hills anticline forced the Columbia River all the way to Wallula Gap from a western route near Goldendale. A western tributary to the Clearwater-Salmon River helped this ancestral river "capture" the Columbia River.

F. During one of many glaciations in the Pleistocene Ice Age. The Columbia River has shifted south of the northernmost extent of Columbia River basalts near Okanogan. The Okanogan Lobe of the Cordilleran Ice Sheet advanced south into northern Washington from British Columbia; although the glacier had gone farther south (onto the Waterville Plateau), it caused a southward shift of the Columbia River of only about 20 miles. The Snake River has been captured by the Salmon River in conjunction with (1) abandonment of the Snake River route through the La Grande Basin of northeastern Oregon, (2) the excavation of Hells Canyon between Oregon and Idaho, and (3) the draining of Lake Idaho in southwestern Idaho.

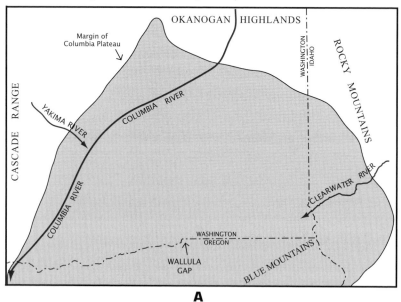

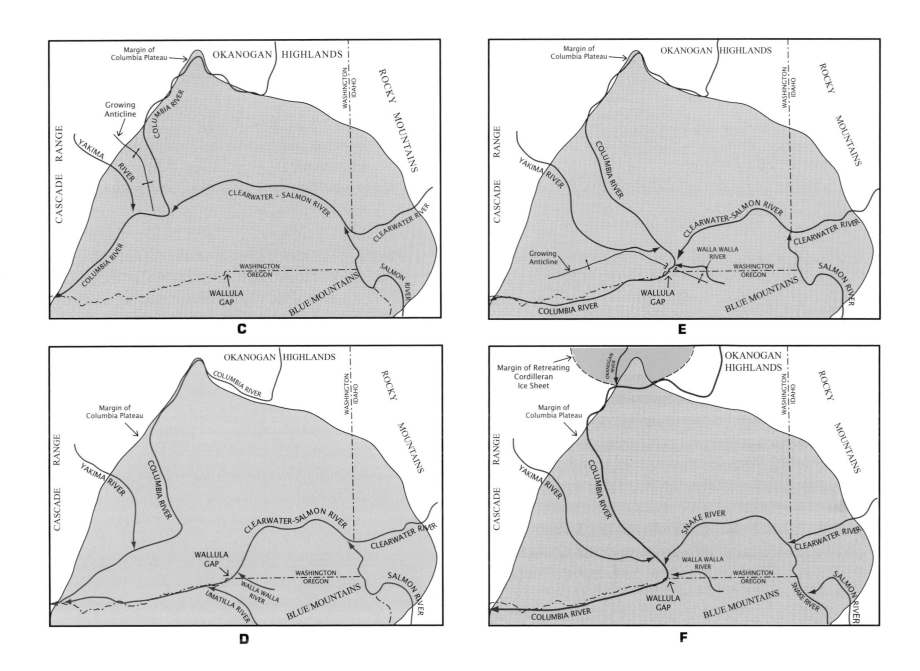

(not evident at Wallula Gap) was buried and baked as Wanapum flows overran the Columbia Basin. In the Wallula Gap area, the Wanapum Basalt has about eight to 10 flows, called the Frenchman Springs Member, which erupted about 15.3 million years ago (see appendix 1: Road Log, mile 12.9). Some of the younger Wanapum flows, present elsewhere on the Columbia Plateau, are not present at Wallula Gap, presumably because the area was too high due to growth of the Horse Heaven Hills Anticline.

At Wallula Gap there is an unconformity, or gap, in the geologic record of about a million years between the Wanapum

At Devils Canyon near Lower Monumental Dam on the Snake River, three intracanyon lava flows fill ancient valleys of the Clearwater-Salmon River. On the left is the Esquatzel flow (about 12.5 million years old); on the lower right is the Pomona flow (about 12 million years old); and on the top is the Elephant Mountain flow (about 10.5 million years old). (Bob Carson photo)

Basalt and the later Saddle Mountains Basalt. Because the Saddle Mountains eruptions spanned more than 5 million years, and because most of the flows were low volume, there was time for rivers to have a major influence on what flows went where and how far.

Wallula Gap is near the center of the area covered by the Umatilla Member, comprised of the two oldest flows of the Saddle Mountains Basalt (see appendix 1: Road Log, mile 14.3). About 14 million years ago, these flows originated at a vent about 90 miles east of Wallula Gap. The lava river widened as it flowed westerly into a lava lake with its northwest shore near Yakima. What valley, if any, did the Umatilla flows follow as they inundated the Wallula area?

The Ellensburg Formation consists of sediments and pyroclastics (volcanic ejecta like ash, pumice, and cinders) interbedded with Columbia River basalts. As stated earlier, pauses in the eruptions of lava flows allowed the accumulation of other materials, including pyroclastics from Cascade volcanoes and stream and lake deposits. During the break of about 2 million years after the Umatilla basalt flows, some Ellensburg Formation accumulated. In places at Wallula Gap as much as 6 feet of ash fell from the air and was partly reworked by water.

Meanwhile, about 50 miles north of the Oregon-Washington state line, a river was cutting a valley west from Idaho to join the Columbia River. This was not the Snake River, which is in this general vicinity today; instead, it was the Clearwater-Salmon River. At least three times between about 14 million and 12 million years ago, the valley of the Clearwater-Salmon River was filled with a lava flow; each time the river cut a new valley, at first near the old lava-filled valley, but later farther south.

At 12 million years ago, the Pomona flow, 170 cubic miles of lava that made it from western Idaho to the Pacific Ocean, entered the scene. This was an intracanyon flow, thick and narrow where it followed the Clearwater-Salmon River course; it is exposed in Devils Canyon just north of Lower Monumental Dam on the Snake River. In the Wallula Gap area, the Pomona flow buried the Umatilla flows and overlying ash. From a lake of Pomona lava to the west, in the subsiding Pasco Basin, a lava river filled an ancestral valley of the Columbia River and made its way to the Pacific. During the next one and a half million years with no basalt flows on the Columbia Plateau, more sediments were deposited. In the Wallula Gap area there is up to 13 feet of silt rich in volcanic ash.

The Clearwater-Salmon River, whose valley had been filled with the Pomona flow, cut yet another valley near the old one. At 10.5 million years ago, the Elephant Mountain intracanyon flow filled the new valley. At Devils Coulee, the Elephant Mountain flow lies atop the Pomona flow, as is the case at Wallula Gap. Like the Pomona flow, the Elephant Mountain flow spread out into a lava lake in the Pasco Basin.

After the Elephant Mountain flow filled the valley, the Clearwater-Salmon River did not give up. As before, it cut another valley; near Lower Monumental Dam, this new valley was filled by the youngest Columbia River basalt. There the 6 million-year-old lava buried gravel and sand deposited by the Clearwater-Salmon River. What was or is this Clearwater-Salmon River that had its valley filled with lava at least four times? The Columbia River was far to the west, the Snake River to the south. The Snake River, from at least 14 million years ago to perhaps only a few million years ago, took a route from the western Snake River Plain, where it is today, northwest through the La Grande Basin in northeastern Oregon.

From there it flowed north, perhaps to the Lewiston Basin in southeastern Washington, or northwest, maybe to the Umatilla Basin in north-central Oregon. If the Columbia and Snake rivers were not near Wallula Gap, what river were the Saddle Mountain lava flows following? Study of the rock types in the sediments under the young lava flow at Lower Monumental Dam indicates that they were deposited by a combination of the Clearwater and Salmon rivers of today that have headwaters in central Idaho. They met at Lewiston, Idaho, but did not include the Snake River as we know it today.

Before this discussion of major rivers in the area, we noted the emplacement of the Elephant Mountain flow at Wallula Gap 10.5 million years ago. No basalt flows came to Wallula Gap for the next 2 million years, so more Ellensburg Formation accumulated, specifically, a local deposit of about 17 feet of silt.

The last lava flow to reach the Wallula Gap area was the Martindale flow of the Ice Harbor Member. The presence of a small remnant of this 8.5 million-year-old basalt at the top of the west side of Wallula Gap means that the Horse Heaven Hills Anticline had not yet risen very high. This flow was likely in the valley of the Clearwater-Salmon River, which was probably at about the elevation of the modern Columbia River.

How did the Columbia River get to Wallula Gap? At the time of eruption of the Martindale flow (about 8.5 million years ago), the Columbia River flowed from the Sentinel Gap area (northwest corner of the Pasco Basin) southwest to the east end of the Columbia River Gorge (near The Dalles, Oregon). The growth of the Yakima folds in this area slowed the Columbia River and caused it to shift east into the subsiding central Pasco Basin. Other factors causing this eastward shift may have included large amounts of sediment being deposited by streams draining the eastern Cascades, and/or blockage of the ancestral Columbia River by basalt flows from the Simcoe Mountains of south-central Washington, where eruptions occurred from 4.5 million to 900,000 years ago.

The river deposited gravel, sand and mud on floodplains and in lakes. These sediments are called the Ringold Formation, which is about 8.5 million to 3.4 million years old. (The Ringold Formation is named for sediments exposed in the White Bluffs near Ringold Flat on the Columbia River opposite the Hanford site.) To get from the central Pasco Basin to Wallula Gap, the Columbia River had to cross the Martindale and other Ice Harbor flows. It might have flowed over them, or a tributary to the Clearwater-Salmon River may have cut through these 8.5 million-year-old flows to "capture" the Columbia River. Either way, the route through Wallula Gap was favored because the elevation here was lower than that of the old route over the Horse Heaven Hills near Goldendale.

It is perhaps strange to think of the mighty Columbia River as a tributary to the Clearwater-Salmon River (today we consider the Clearwater and Salmon rivers to be only in Idaho). The addition of the discharge of the Columbia River to the Clearwater-Salmon River made it easier for the river (we shall now call it the Columbia) to downcut as the Horse Heaven Hills continued to rise. The result is the water gap, with sides about 1,000 feet high. The floor of this water gap, the pre-dam floodplain of the Columbia River, is at an elevation of 300 feet. The lowest point (Satus Pass) in the western Horse Heaven Hills, where the Columbia River used to be, has an elevation of 3,107 feet. So the Horse Heaven Hills Anticline has risen at least 2,800 feet near Satus Pass and at least 800 feet at Wallula Gap. The Columbia River crosses the lowest part of the Horse Heaven Hills.

How did the Snake River cut Hells Canyon and join the Columbia River in the Pasco Basin? Today the Snake River enters the Columbia above Wallula Gap, but during the eruption of the Columbia River basalts, the Snake went elsewhere. The area southeast of Wallula Gap has been rising for tens of millions of years; if the Snake River had been flowing across northeastern Oregon, this uplift likely would have slowed it. Meanwhile, at the present location of Hells Canyon between Idaho and Oregon, a major north-flowing tributary to the Salmon River was cutting a valley and extending its headwaters southward. Think of an eroding gully on a steep slope: The water and sediment go downhill, but the head of the gully moves uphill. Giant Lake Idaho existed in southern Idaho for millions of years until it drained about 2 million years ago. Although the Snake River may have been cutting Hells Canyon for as much as 6 million years, it is more likely that a tributary to the Salmon River captured the Snake River and started draining Lake Idaho only 2 million or 3 million years ago. The draining of Lake Idaho and the addition of Snake River drainage to the Salmon River would have facilitated downcutting of Hells Canyon. The continuing uplift of the Blue Mountains region plus the erosion by the Snake River has made Hells Canyon one of the deepest gorges in North America. The drop from the top of Idaho's Seven Devils Mountains to the bottom of Hells Canyon is more than 8,000 feet!

Glaciers, Loess and Floods

Between the end of deposition of the Ringold Formation 3.4 million years ago and the beginning of the most recent ice age about

2 million years ago, we have no known rocks or sediments that record geologic history in the Wallula area. The last period of Earth's history is called the Quaternary, which began about 2 million years ago (officially, 1.6 million years ago, but a few geologists prefer an earlier date). The terms the *Quaternary* (a period), the *Pleistocene* (an epoch ending 12,000 years ago), and the *Ice Age* are often used interchangeably because of the extensive glaciation at this time. However, this was only the most recent ice age. Ice ages occurred in the early Precambrian (about 2.5 billion years ago) and late Precambrian (about 800 million years ago), as well as in the late Paleozoic (about 300 million years ago). Each *ice age* lasts millions of years, with alternating *glaciations* and *interglaciations*. During the current Ice Age, the glacial-interglacial cycle is about 100,000 years, so there have been perhaps as many as 20 glaciations in the last 2 million years. The last glaciation began about 100,000 years ago and ended about 12,000 years ago; the *Holocene*, the most recent epoch (12,000 years ago to the present) of geologic history, coincides with the current interglaciation. About 30 percent of the Earth was covered by glaciers at the peak of each glaciation, whereas only 10 percent of the Earth (mostly Antarctica and Greenland) is covered during an interglaciation.

What does glaciation have to do with Wallula if the nearest glaciers were about 85 miles away in the Wallowa Mountains of northeastern Oregon? To start with, the climate was colder during glaciations, so different plants lived in the Wallula area. Many large herbivores, such as mammoths and mastodons, lived in this vicinity. Most of the large mammals except bison became extinct about 12,000 years ago, more likely due to hunting by American Indians than to climate change. (The horses in North America also became extinct, but they were reintroduced by the Spanish much later.) No mass extinction is associated with similar climate changes at the ends of earlier glaciations. Humans did not arrive here until perhaps about 14,000 years ago.

The deposition of loess in eastern Washington and Oregon began in the Pleistocene. Loess is wind-deposited silt, usually massive because it is bioturbated by plants and animals (silts deposited in lakes are more likely to be layered). To deposit loess, the wind needs a source of silt, and that was provided by glaciers. Rock flour is silt-sized sediment abraded as glaciers drag loose rocks over bedrock. Glaciers existed in the Cascades, all over British Columbia

Loess is wind-deposited silt. This tan, massive sediment has crude columnar joints near the top and a light-colored, buried soil beneath that is rich in caliche (calcium carbonate). (Bob Carson photo)

and in the northern Rockies. From the British Columbia glacier (called the Cordilleran Ice Sheet), tongues of ice flowed south over the Okanogan Highlands of northeastern Washington, and into northern Idaho and northwestern Montana. The rock flour, suspended in the meltwater released from all this ice, came down rivers – the Yakima to the west, the Columbia to the north and the Snake to the east. All this meltwater came together in the Pasco Basin, and went down the Columbia River through Wallula Gap to the Umatilla Basin, and on through the Columbia River Gorge to a lower Pacific Ocean. (The connection between sea level and the amount of ice on the continents is intimate: at the peak of each glaciation, sea level was about 400 feet below present.) The annual variation in meltwater was substantial – high discharges during summer melting and low discharges during the frozen winters. Imagine the floodplain of the Columbia River from the Pasco Basin to the Umatilla Basin during these two seasons. In summer the floodplain was inundated with turbid water loaded with rock flour, like today's Hoh River on the Olympic Peninsula or the White River draining Mount Rainier. Any vegetation that started growing in the spring would be under water; any plants surviving into autumn would be dead or dormant in winter. The water level dropped so that the river, likely covered with ice, was restricted to a few channels between islands. With little vegetation, most of the floodplain was susceptible to wind erosion. Sand was transported a short distance to form dunes at the edge of the floodplain. The prevailing southwest winds suspended the rock flour or silt and carried it high and far. From the Umatilla Basin, silt was transported to the top of the Horse Heaven Hills, where it makes a soil superb for growing wheat. From both the Umatilla and Pasco Basins, silt was transported northeast to eastern Washington. As the silt settled out of suspension from the air column, it blanketed preexisting topography.

Loess deposition has been going on throughout the Quaternary – for about 2 million years. The greatest thickness of loess, perhaps 300 feet, occurs in the Palouse Hills of eastern Washington, downwind of the source areas along the Columbia River. Some think that the Palouse Hills are gigantic dunes, but, as stated before, the silt is deposited as a blanket over the pre-existing landscape. The hills in the area result from dissection by running water. Loess deposition was not constant over time. After great floods (more later), there was so much sediment in the source areas that the rate of loess deposition dramatically increased. At other times the rate of deposition was so slow that the ground surface was stable enough for soils to form. In this dry climate, the soils became enriched in caliche, or calcium carbonate. Ash layers interbedded with the loess record eruptions of Cascade volcanoes and help geologists to date the loess. Within the loess there are fossils of rodents, land snails and plants.

Much of the topography of the Wallula area was shaped by what may have been the Earth's greatest floods, some perhaps 20 times as large as the present discharge of all the world's rivers combined. J Harlen Bretz studied glaciation of western Washington during the second decade of the 1900s, and then he turned his attention to eastern Washington in the 1920s. Bretz knew that there had been huge floods across eastern Washington, but it took decades for him to determine the source of the floodwaters. Then it took decades more for most geologists to believe the results of his research. Although geologists agree that there were floods now and then throughout the Pleistocene, they disagree about how many floods occurred during the last flood episode near the end of the Pleistocene.

A tongue of the Cordilleran Ice Sheet advanced south from British Columbia down through northern Idaho, carving Priest Lake and Lake Pend Oreille. This Pend Oreille Lobe of ice terminated at Cabinet Gorge on the Idaho-Montana border, where it blocked Clark Fork River (this would be Clark Fork of the Columbia, not Clarks Fork of the Yellowstone River on the east side of the Continental Divide). The Pend Oreille Lobe was about 2,000 feet thick at Cabinet Gorge, so a huge lake was created upriver to the east and south. Glacial Lake Missoula, with an area of 3,000 square miles, stretched up the Clark Fork well past Missoula (where the water was 950 feet deep), and had arms extending south up the

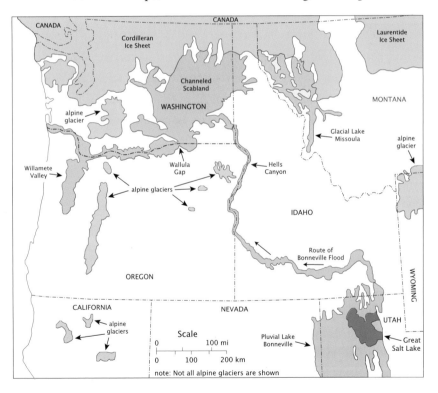

Bitterroot Valley and north almost to Flathead Lake. With this extent, and a water depth of nearly 2,000 feet at the ice dam, its volume of more than 500 cubic miles was comparable to the size of one of the Great Lakes.

Once Clark Fork was dammed, the level of Glacial Lake Missoula rose. Because ice is less dense than water, when the lake got almost as deep as the glacier dam was thick, the ice started to float, allowing the lake to drain under the huge ice dam causing thermal and physical erosion. The thermal erosion occurred because the lake

Glaciers and floods in the Pacific Northwest about 15,000 years ago. In green are shown most of the glaciers that existed in the region. From smallest to largest, they are alpine glaciers that existed in the Cascade Range, northeastern Oregon, northwestern Wyoming and elsewhere; the Cordilleran Ice Sheet, centered on British Columbia; and the Laurentide Ice Sheet, which stretched from Montana to Greenland. A lobe of the Cordilleran Ice Sheet advanced south through northern Idaho to block Montana's Clark Fork and dam Glacial Lake Missoula (light blue), which broke through the glacier dam. The filling and emptying of Glacial Lake Missoula occurred dozens of times during each of multiple glaciations of the Pleistocene Ice Age. In brown is shown the area covered by each flood from Glacial Lake Missoula. The floods raced across northern Idaho, spread across Washington's Channeled Scabland, and converged at the hydraulic dam at Wallula Gap. The bottleneck at Wallula Gap caused the floodwaters to back up the Walla Walla, Yakima and other valleys. From Wallula Gap the floods overwhelmed the Umatilla Basin, roared through the Columbia River Gorge, and inundated Oregon's Willamette Valley before pouring into a lower Pacific Ocean. The Bonneville Flood (purple) from Utah is different in many respects. First, it was not from a glacial lake; pluvial Lake Bonneville (light blue) rose in a closed basin because the climate was cooler and/or moister. (In dark blue is the Great Salt Lake; today's warm, dry climate has resulted in this small, shallow, saline remnant of Lake Bonneville.) Second, the Bonneville Flood occurred only once, when Lake Bonneville overflowed its northern rim about 15,000 years ago. Third, compared with the Missoula Floods, the deluge from Utah was smaller but lasted longer (about a month). The Bonneville Flood traveled west across the Snake River Plain of southern Idaho and north through Hells Canyon of the Snake River. Although it certainly reached the Pacific Ocean, evidence for the flood downstream of Lewiston, Idaho, was wiped out by later Missoula Floods. (After Carson and Pogue, 1996) was slightly warmer than freezing and, therefore, melted the bottom of the glacier. The physical erosion was due to the high velocity and great turbulence of the water. The failure of the ice dam released a gigantic flood carrying huge icebergs. This flood had a discharge of at least 600 million and perhaps 750 million cubic feet per second (15 to 18 cubic miles of water per hour)! Glacial Lake Missoula drained in only about three days. Compare that with the mean discharge of the Columbia River (265,000 cubic feet per second) and its flood-of-record (1.2 million cubic feet per second in 1894). The Icelandic word jökulhlaup means glacier outburst flood. Subglacial volcanic eruptions produce the most infamous jökulhlaups in Iceland.

Cross beds showing current direction to the right in a Missoula floods sand and gravel bar. This photo, taken by the Arnold Studio circa 1940, is labeled "Desert sand dune near Attalia (located close to the Columbia River between Wallula and Attalia)." (Fred L. Mitchell Collection)

Imagine that island with a temporary river larger than the Amazon. Such has happened many times in the thousand-year human history of Iceland, most recently when Grimsvotn – a volcano – erupted beneath Vatnajokull – a glacier – in 1996. The discharge was more than 1.5 million cubic feet per second, larger than the Columbia River's historic record flood. Many Cascade volcanoes are subject to jökulhlaups, usually when warm weather or heavy rains trigger the release of water from cavities within or beneath a glacier. There are no volcanoes near Cabinet Gorge, but the ice dam failure caused a whopper of a jökulhlaup.

We will follow a typical Missoula flood from Glacial Lake Missoula to the Pacific Ocean. In general, where the catastrophic flood from Glacial Lake Missoula was going the fastest, there was erosion. Where the flood slowed a little, it deposited a gravel bar. Where the flood slowed a lot, it deposited fine-grained slackwater sediments.

The icy flood rushed southwest across northern Idaho, dumping sediment up tributary valleys, damming their mouths to create Coeur d'Alene Lake and smaller lakes. At Spokane the flood divided to cross the Columbia Plateau. Roughly a third of the water jumped a drainage divide to the south, then followed the Palouse River to its mouth; there the flood rushed up the Snake River to Hells Canyon and down the Snake River to the Pasco Basin. About a third of the floodwater going through Spokane rushed west into Glacial Lake Columbia, caused by the damming of the Columbia River at Grand Coulee Dam by the Okanogan Lobe of the Cordilleran Ice Sheet. As the lake was already full, floodwaters poured down Grand Coulee over Dry Falls and divided in the Quincy Basin, taking different routes south to the Pasco Basin. The rest of the water inundating Spokane went southwesterly along many paths between the Palouse River route and the Grand Coulee route.

The combined width of these many floodwater paths across eastern Washington was tens of miles. The 15 to 18 cubic miles of water per hour all entered the Pasco Basin, whose only exit was Wallula Gap, with a valley floor width of less than one mile. Wallula Gap became the biggest dam in Earth's history, a hydraulic dam because the flood could not leave the Pasco Basin as fast as it arrived, so a very temporary Lake Lewis was created north of the Horse Heaven Hills. As the water level rose to an elevation of about 1,250 feet, Lake Lewis attained a volume of almost 300 cubic miles. Even with water 950 feet deep rushing through Wallula Gap, the discharge could reach only about 350 million cubic feet per second (more than 8 cubic miles per hour), or about half of the discharge into Lake Lewis. With the water velocity perhaps exceeding 75 miles per hour, erosion was severe. While the lower walls of Wallula Gap were being eroded, a spectacular landscape was being created as the floodwaters spread over the top edges. Present along much of the water gap but particularly prominent on both sides of the north end is a channeled scabland (see appendix 1: Road Log, mile 12.9). Flood channels weave an intricate pattern around erosion remnants (scabs) of basalt flows. The flood scoured closed depressions on many of the channel floors, which have scabs rising 100 feet and more above them. This local channeled scabland is a miniature edition of eastern Washington's giant Channeled Scabland studied by J Harlen Bretz. The Grand Coulee dwarfs the little side channels at Wallula Gap, and Steamboat Rock is an erosion remnant more than a thousand times larger than the Twin Sisters.

The hydraulic dam at Wallula Gap caused significant deposition because the floodwaters slowed in Lake Lewis, dropping most of their sediment (see appendix 1: Road Log, mile 15.4). In each bed (typically one to five feet thick) of this slackwater sediment, the grain size decreases (often from sand to silt) from bottom to top because the current was slowing. Arms of Lake Lewis extended up the Yakima and Walla Walla Valleys, where a lot of slackwater

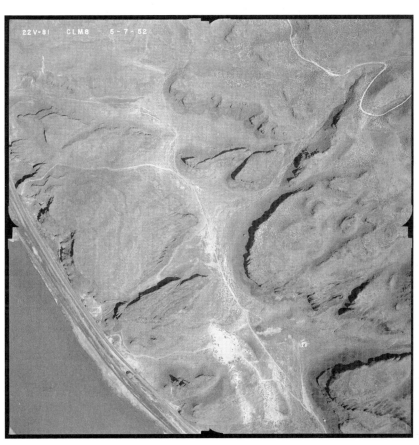

Vertical air photo of the Twin Sisters area, May 7, 1952. North is to the upper left. The Twin Sisters are in lower center near the Columbia River. Nearby the light areas are sand dunes. Shadows line the cliffs that form a miniature channeled scabland as a result of erosion by the Missoula floods. (Army Corps of Engineers)

sediment was deposited. At many places in the Pacific Northwest – in Glacial Lake Columbia of northern Washington, in Lake Lewis of southern Washington, in the nearby Umatilla Basin, and in the Willamette Valley of western Oregon – there are tens of beds of slackwater sediments. The beds belong to different flood episodes over hundreds of thousands of years. Sediments of the oldest-known flood episode must be older than 780,000 years, because their magnetic polarity is reversed.

The slackwater sediments of the latest flood episode are called the Touchet Beds (see appendix 1: Road Log, miles 14.3 and 15.4), named for exposures along the Walla Walla River just south of the town of Touchet. Nearby, in a place called Burlingame Canyon, there

Vertical air photo of the Wallula Junction area, October 13, 1953. North is to the lower left. The Olympic-Wallowa lineament runs from right center to top center. The island in the lower right is being drowned by rising Lake Wallula, as is the lower Walla Walla valley in the upper left. The street pattern shows where the old town of Wallula is being submerged. Note old and new highway and railroad bridges over the mouth of the Walla Walla River. (Army Corps of Engineers)

Above both sides of the Columbia River is a miniature channeled scabland, including the Twin Sisters in left center. In this early 1950s photograph, note the small dune fields of light-colored sand blown from sand and gravel bars along the shores of the river. (Army Corps of Engineers)

are 40 Touchet Beds. Elsewhere there are as many as 89 Touchet Beds. One of the greatest geologic debates of the last century has been about how many Missoula floods it took to account for all the Touchet Beds. At one time or another, J Harlen Bretz and other geologists stated that all the Touchet Beds were deposited by one late Pleistocene Missoula flood. In 1980, Richard Waitt (U.S. Geological Survey) argued that the presence of Mount St. Helens ash between two of the Touchet Beds proved that there had to be more than one flood, and that, most likely, each Touchet Bed represented a separate flood. Patrick Spencer, of Whitman College, used fossil rodent bones and burrows within the Touchet Beds to support Waitt's hypothesis. The Mount St. Helens ash within the Touchet Beds is 13,000 years old; in places, two layers of ash represent two eruptions from the

volcanic peak in southwestern Washington. The magnetic properties of these ash layers indicate that they fell decades apart, further supporting Waitt's conclusions.

As mentioned before, part of the floodwaters from Glacial Lake Missoula dumped into Glacial Lake Columbia. Typical sediments in glacial lakes consist of thin rhythmic beds deposited in an annual cycle: sandier in the summer when melting glaciers discharge a lot of water and sediment; finer-grained in the winter when discharge is greatly reduced, and the lake surface is frozen. Such cyclic beds, or *varves*, are exposed along the Sanpoil Arm of modern Lake Roosevelt, the reservoir impounded by Grand Coulee Dam. This varved sediment deposited in Glacial Lake Columbia was studied by Brian Atwater (U.S. Geological Survey), who found

The miniature channeled scabland near the Twin Sisters. (Whitman College and Northwest Archives)

A channel high above the north end of the west side of Wallula Gap. The high-velocity waters of the Missoula floods eroded this channel through basalt flows. (Bob Carson photo)

Touchet Beds in the Walla Walla Valley. **Top Left:** Each bed was deposited by a Missoula flood. **Top Right:** Between two of the beds is ash erupted from Mount St. Helens about 13,000 years ago. **Bottom:** Cutting across the Touchet Beds are clastic dikes, perhaps injected during a large, prehistoric earthquake. (Bob Carson photos)

A clastic dike in a basalt flow. The silt with chunks of basalt probably filled the crack during an earthquake. (Bob Carson photo)

that the varves were interrupted by flood deposits similar to the Touchet Beds. Atwater not only further demonstrated that each massive bed represented a separate flood, but he also determined the number of years between floods by counting the varves. Decades separate the earliest floods, but the intervals shorten with later floods. The Touchet Beds exposed in Burlingame Canyon in the Walla Walla Valley are thicker at the base and thinner at the top. The evidence from both places suggests that later floods were smaller and more frequent, probably because as the Pend Oreille Lobe of the Cordilleran Ice Sheet retreated north, ice dams got smaller. Therefore, it would not have taken as long for Glacial Lake Missoula to fill and float the glacier terminus. Thus a smaller glacial lake would release a smaller jökulhlaup. Another possible explanation for thinner Touchet Beds later in the last flood episode is that each passing flood left less sediment to be eroded.

Clastic dikes are common in the Touchet Beds and rare in the basalts. Clastic dikes are different than igneous dikes of magma intruded through pre-existing rocks. Clastic dikes are water-saturated sediment that is injected upward or downward into preexisting sediments or rocks. The clastic dikes in the Touchet Beds are typically layered sand and silt. At the southwestern end of Wallula Gap, the clastic dikes in a lava flow resemble chunky peanut butter. Kevin Pogue, of Whitman College, argues that the clastic dikes may have been injected during a large prehistoric earthquake.

Each jökulhlaup carried a lot of silt and sand suspended in the turbulent waters. The primary source of the silt was the loess blanket in eastern Washington, particularly where the Palouse Hills were low enough to be overtopped by the floods. Here we have an interesting case of sediment recycling: The jökulhlaups eroded the loess and transported part of it southwest to the Pasco and Umatilla Basins; then the prevailing winds eroded the silt from these basins and transported it back to the northeast. After each flood episode there was a huge supply of silt for the wind to erode from the basins and redeposit in the Palouse Hills. The wind also transported sand toward the northeast, but only for relatively short distances since the wind moves sand by bouncing, rolling, and sliding the grains over the surface. In contrast, wind entrains silt particles high in the air by suspension.

The jökulhlaups also carried particles coarser than sand, including huge boulders. For example, the floods slowed just south of the Grand Coulee and deposited a spectacular fan of boulders. Although the floods were going so fast through Wallula Gap that erosion generally dominated, there are local gravel deposits where the floods slowed. Most of the coarser particles were ripped from nearby basalt bedrock, but many are exotic clasts like granite and quartzite, transported from far away. Some of the largest exotic clasts rode icebergs atop the floods. Many icebergs were stranded in Juniper Canyon, leaving boulders up to 6 feet long, some at elevations more than 1,000 feet (see appendix 1: Road Log, mile 4.5); most of these boulders are granitic. Jim O'Connor (U.S. Geological Survey) found an iceberg-rafted, buffalo-sized granitic erratic at the top of the cliffs (elevation 1,120 feet) on the west side of the northern end of Wallula Gap!

At the top of Wallula Gap, the floodwaters averaged about two miles wide. Imagine riding a raft at 75 miles per hour in a rapid that drops 150 feet in 10 miles, with the shore a mile away. It is estimated that this white water (more like chocolate milk) lasted only the five days that it took Lake Lewis to drain. As the torrents slowed

Granitic erratic in Juniper Canyon. This boulder rode an iceberg to an elevation of 1,000 feet, about 700 feet above the floor of the Columbia River. (Bob Carson photo)

in dead-end tributary canyons, they deposited eddy bars. There are many, large eddy bars alongside Wallula Gap, including one in Spring Gulch (see appendix 1: Road Log, mile 10.1) and another in Juniper Canyon. Erosion by the intermittent stream in Juniper Canyon has removed most of that eddy bar. The steep fronts of the eddy bars face the Columbia River and are as much as 400 feet high. The flat tops slope gently up the dead-end canyons for a half mile or more. Since deposition, gullies have partly dissected the eddy bars to expose the sediments within them. This sediment is mostly crudely bedded, angular basalt cobbles, but the grain size ranges from silt to boulders. Mixed with the basalt clasts are scattered exotic stones like gneiss, granite and quartzite. The sediments in the eddy bars are part of a geologic unit called the Pasco Gravels.

Where did the jökulhlaups go from Wallula Gap? The first place was the wide Umatilla Basin, where they deposited sediments in a temporary lake that rose to an elevation of about 1,100 feet, due to the hydraulic damming effect of the relatively narrow Columbia River Gorge downstream. The floodwaters rushed up tributary valleys; for example, an iceberg came to rest 60 miles up the John Day River. As the jökulhlaups plunged down the Columbia River Gorge, they caused considerable erosion. A constriction along the lower Columbia River caused the floodwaters to inundate the Willamette Valley as far south as Eugene. From there the floods rushed down the Columbia past Astoria and across what is now the continental shelf to a lower Pacific Ocean.

There was one more giant flood in this area during the late Pleistocene, but it was not a jökulhlaup. With a volume of only about 1,100 cubic miles, the Bonneville Flood was small in comparison with Missoula floods. Lake Bonneville was a pluvial

Eddy bars deposited by the Missoula floods are as much as 600 feet above the Columbia River. **A:** Air photo of gravel bar filling pre-flood valley on the west side of Wallula Gap. **B:** A tug pushes barges down Lake Wallula, the crew unaware of the huge gravel bar above them. In left center below the gullies in the eddy bar is an alluvial fan, with a white layer of 7,700-year-old Mazama ash from Crater Lake. **C:** The inside of the eddy bar at Spring Gulch. The gravels were deposited as Missoula floods raced through Wallula Gap. The light-colored, fine-grained sediments settled out of suspension as the floods waned, but the next floods brought more gravel. (Bob Carson photos)

Tammany Bar on the Snake River just south of Lewiston, Idaho. At the bottom are gravels deposited by the Bonneville flood from Utah; the giant cross beds dipping north show the current direction. The horizontal layers of sand and silt above the gravels are Touchet Beds, slackwater sediments deposited because the waters of Missoula floods backed up behind the hydraulic dam at Wallula Gap. At the top are a few feet of loess, silt deposited by the wind since the last flood inundated Lewiston. (Bob Carson photo)

Sand dunes north of the mouth of the Walla Walla River. This photo, taken by the Arnold Studio in the 1930s, was hand colored by Mrs. Arnold. (Fred L. Mitchell Collection)

Oblique air photo of Wallula Gap before McNary Dam. The Walla Walla River (lower left) is in flood, but the Columbia River is relatively low. Note the sand dunes in the foreground and the rock ledges of basalt below and opposite the mouth of the Walla Walla River. (Fred L. Mitchell Collection)

lake, not a glacial lake. Pluvial lakes are high during the cool, moist conditions of a glaciation and shrink to well below their outlets during warm dry interglacial periods. Lake Bonneville covered much of Utah; the Great Salt Lake is its remnant. About 14,500 years ago, Lake Bonneville overflowed at Red Rock Pass in southeastern Idaho. The Bonneville Flood followed the Snake River across southern Idaho, rushed north through Hells Canyon, and deposited a huge gravel bar just south of Lewiston, Idaho. Downriver from there, its record was eroded or buried by later Missoula floods. The Bonneville Flood, with a discharge of about 35 million cubic feet per second at Red Rock Pass, had decreased to about half that by the time it got to Wallula Gap (compare this with the 1894 Columbia River flood of 1.2 million cubic feet per second). There is no visible evidence for the Bonneville Flood at Wallula Gap, but it had to go through the water gap.

After the Floods

Twelve thousand years ago is the arbitrary geologic boundary between the Pleistocene Epoch (the "Ice Age") and the Holocene, the present epoch of the Earth's history. At 12,000 years ago, the edges of the big glaciers were retreating north across the U.S.-Canada border. Humans were already on the scene in the Pacific Northwest, but as hunter-gatherers without agriculture or domesticated livestock, they had little effect on the geologic environment. Early Americans did, however, have major direct effects on the fauna and flora in that they hunted large herbivores and set fires. The term Holocene implies post-glacial. In this area a useful geologic boundary is post-flood – after the last of the Touchet Beds was deposited about 12,700 years ago.

The deposition of loess continued from the Pleistocene into the Holocene. Indeed, all the Touchet Beds in the Yakima and Walla Walla valleys and the Pasco and Umatilla basins were an abundant source of loess for the Palouse Hills and elsewhere. Places that were not overtopped by the Missoula floods, like the crest of the Horse Heaven Hills, received more silt on top of the Pleistocene loess. Where the jökulhlaups had swept the surface clean of loose sediment, on channel floors for example, the Holocene loess became valuable soil.

The wind also deposited dunes in various places, using the sand supply from sandbars along the Columbia and Snake rivers. The Juniper Dunes, one of the two largest dune fields in Washington, are downwind (northeast) of the Pasco Basin. A small dune field in the vicinity of the Twin Sisters (see appendix 1: Road Log, mile 12.6-12.7) was formed from sandbars on the east side of the Columbia River; because the bars are now drowned by the reservoir, there is no more sand supply, and the dunes are becoming vegetated and inactive. This site was favored for dunes because it lacks the high cliffs common elsewhere along Wallula Gap; also, the prevailing southwesterly winds are funneled along the water gap toward this area. The largest dune field at Wallula Gap is along the south side of Juniper Canyon (see appendix 1: Road Log, mile 4.5). Here the sand is blown from the Umatilla Basin and accumulates on the lee (north) side of the basalt ridge south of the canyon. Much of this dune field is stabilized, but there are several areas of bare sand. Sand cannot "walk on water," so the dunes are not able to migrate across the creek.

The Missoula floods cleaned out Wallula Gap; that is, the high-velocity turbulent water eroded all loose sediment and

Talus at the base of the Twin Sisters. (Dianne Kornberg photo)

some bedrock in the water gap (an exception is the deposition of the eddy bars in side canyons). After the last Missoula flood, "normal" geologic processes resumed. Freeze-thaw and other types of weathering weakened the cliff faces and liberated rocks, which fell into growing *taluses,* sloping heaps of angular rock fragments at the bases of cliffs. At more than 250 feet high, some are the largest taluses for tens of miles in all directions.

The walls of Wallula Gap have been cut by intermittent streams. The side canyons all along the water gap got their starts before the Missoula floods, and, as noted, the jökulhlaups filled some with eddy bars. Large gullies cross the eddy bars, with the largest intermittent stream having removed most of the eddy bar in Juniper Canyon. Some of the sediment eroded by the intermittent streams was carried all the way to the pre-dam Columbia River, but much of it accumulated in alluvial fans at the canyon and gully mouths (see appendix 1: Road Log, mile 8.8).

Alluvial fans are gently sloping landforms with semicircular or triangular plan (map) views. Located at the base of steep slopes like those along Wallula Gap, they are deposited by intermittent streams. These streams are torrents during heavy rains or if there happens to be rapid snowmelt. As long as the water is confined by canyon (or gully) sides, there is little sediment deposited, but once the torrent spreads out beyond the canyon mouth, rocks and mud are dumped. The largest particles are usually deposited near the apex of the alluvial fan at the canyon mouth.

Railroad cuts in the large alluvial fans on the west side of Wallula Gap reveal white bands of fine-grained material. This Mazama ash was blown high into the atmosphere during the eruption that produced Crater Lake 7,700 years ago. The ash was

View south from Wallula of the water gap and the Horse Heaven Hills. (John Clement photo)

carried northeasterly by the prevailing winds and settled over wide areas of Oregon, Washington and beyond. Most of the inch or so of volcanic ash that fell on the Horse Heaven Hills was washed off the uplands and down the canyons to accumulate on the alluvial fans (see appendix 1: Road Log, mile 8.8). Subsequent deposition buried the ash, but it is visible in cuts in the alluvial fans.

As noted before, the supply of sand for dunes at Wallula Gap has been drowned, but other processes continue. Intensive agriculture in eastern Washington and Oregon means bare fields here and there at various times of the year; during each dust storm, the wind erodes these fields, suspends the silt in the atmosphere,

and deposits another thin blanket of loess on the landscape. Rocks occasionally fall from cliffs into taluses. Flash floods erode canyons and transfer the sediment to alluvial fans.

The last major geologic event to occur at Wallula Gap was not related to the eruptions of Mount St. Helens in 1980, for little ash fell that far south in Washington. Rather, it was the filling of Lake Wallula behind McNary Dam in 1953. The reservoir drowned the floodplains of the Columbia River and the lowermost Walla Walla River. The Columbia never recovered, but the high sediment load of the Walla Walla allowed it to fill its drowned valley and prograde a delta out into Lake Wallula (see appendix 1: Road Log, mile 15.0). In the still reservoir, a half century of mud blankets the sand and gravel bars that shifted for thousands of years during the annual cycles of changing depths and discharges of the Columbia River. The great bend and gap survive; the small bends and bars are drowned.

Mazama ash in an alluvial fan at the Oregon-Washington state line. After the Missoula floods cleaned out Wallula Gap, sediment again began to accumulate at the base of the basalt cliffs. Here an intermittent stream deposited an alluvial fan, in which there is Mazama ash washed off the hills above after the eruption at Crater Lake 7,700 years ago. (Bob Carson photo)

Bibliography

Allen, J.E., Marjorie Burns and S.C. Sargent, 1986, *Cataclysms on the Columbia: A layman's guide to the features produced by the catastrophic Bretz floods in the Pacific Northwest*: Portland, Oregon, Timber Press, 211 p.

Alt, D.D. and D.W. Hyndman, 1978, *Roadside geology of Oregon*: Missoula, Montana, Mountain Press, 268 p.

Alt, D.D. and D.W. Hyndman, 1984, *Roadside geology of Washington*: Missoula, Montana, Mountain Press, 282 p.

Babcock, Scott and Bob Carson, 2000, *Hiking Washington's geology*: Seattle, The Mountaineers, 272 p.

Baker, V.R., 1983, "Late-Pleistocene fluvial systems," *in* S.C. Porter, ed., *The late Pleistocene*, v. 1 *of* H.E. Wright, Jr., ed., *Late-Quaternary environments of the United States*: Minneapolis, Minnesota, University of Minnesota Press, p. 115-129.

Baker, V.R. and Dag Nummendal, 1978, *The Channeled Scabland: A guide to the geomorphology of the Columbia Basin*: Washington, National Aeronautics and Space Administration, 186 p.

Baldwin, E.M., 1981, *Geology of Oregon*: Dubuque, Iowa, Kendall/Hunt Publishing Company, 170 p.

Benito, Gerardo and J.E. O'Connor, 2003, "Number and size of last-glacial Missoula floods in the Columbia River valley between the Pasco Basin, Washington, and Portland, Oregon": *Geological Society of America Bulletin*, v. 115, no. 5, p. 624-638.

Bishop, E.M., 2003, *In search of ancient Oregon: A geological and natural history*: Portland, Oregon, Timber Press, 288 p.

Bishop, E.M. and J.E. Allen, 2004, *Hiking Oregon's geology*: Seattle, The Mountaineers, 276 p.

Bjornstad, B.N., 2006, *On the trail of the Ice Age floods: A geological field guide to the Mid-Columbia Basin*: Sandpoint, Idaho, Keokee Company Publishing, 308 p.

Bretz, J H., 1923, "The Channeled Scablands of the Columbia Plateau": *Journal of Geology*, v. 31, p. 617-649.

Bretz, J H., 1959, *Washington's Channeled Scabland*: Washington Division of Mines and Geology Bulletin 45, 57 p.

Brown, B.H., 1937, "The State-Line earthquake at Milton and Walla Walla": *Seismological Society of America Bulletin*, v. 237, p. 205-209.

Carson, R.J. and K.R. Pogue, 1996, *Flood basalts and glacier floods: Roadside geology of parts of Walla Walla, Franklin, and Columbia Counties, Washington*: Washington Division of Geology and Earth Resources Information Circular 90, 47 p.

Fecht, K.R., S.P. Reidel and A.M. Tallman, 1987, "Paleodrainage of the Columbia River system on the Columbia Plateau of Washington State – a summary," *in* J.E. Schuster, ed., *Selected papers on the geology of Washington*: Washington Division of Geology and Earth Resources Bulletin 77, p. 219-248.

Ferns, M.L., V.S. McConnell and I.P. Madin, in review, *Geology of the Umatilla River basin, Morrow, Umatilla, and Union Counties, Oregon*: Oregon Department of Geology and Mineral Industries Open-File Report.

Gardner, J.N., M.G. Snow and K.R. Fecht, 1981, *Geology of the Wallula Gap Area, Washington*: Rockwell Hanford Operations, Richland, Washington, Document RHO-BWI-LD-9, 67 p.

Hooper, P.R., 1997, "The Columbia River flood basalt province: current status," *in* J.J. Mahoney and M.F. Coffin, eds., *Large igneous provinces: Continental, oceanic, and planetary flood volcanism*: American Geophysical Union, Geophysical Monograph 100, p. 1-27.

Hooper, P.R., V.E. Camp, S.P. Reidel and M.E. Ross, 2007, "The origin of the Columbia River flood basalt province: Plume versus nonplume models," *in* G.R. Foulger and D.M. Jurdy, eds., *Plates, plumes, and planetary processes*: Geological Society of America Special Paper 430, p. 635-668.

Jordan, B.T., 2005, "Age-progressive volcanism of the Oregon High Lava Plains: Overview and evaluation of tectonic models," *in* G.R. Foulger, J.H. Natland, D.C. Presnall and D.L. Anderson, eds., *Plates, plumes, and paradigms*: Geological Society of America Special Paper 388, p. 503-515.

Jordan, B.T., A.L. Grunder, R.A. Duncan and A.L. Deino, 2004, "Geochronology of age-progressive volcanism of the Oregon High Lava Plains: Implications for the plume interpretation of Yellowstone": *Journal of Geophysical Research*, v.109, B10202, 19 p.

Mueller, Marge, and Ted Mueller, 1997, *Fire, faults, and floods: A road and trail guide exploring the origins of the Columbia River Basin*: Moscow, Idaho, University of Idaho Press, 288 p.

O'Connor, J.E., 1993, *Hydrology, hydraulics, and geomorphology of the Bonneville Flood*: Geological Society of America Special Paper 274, 83 p.

O'Connor, J.E. and V.R. Baker, 1992, "Magnitudes and implications of peak discharges from glacial Lake Missoula": *Geological Society of America Bulletin*, v. 104, p. 267-279.

Orr, E.L. and W.N. Orr, 2002, *Geology of the Pacific Northwest*: New York, McGraw-Hill, 409 p.

Raisz, E.J., 1945, "The Olympic Wallowa Lineament": *American Journal of Science*, v. 243A, p. 479-485.

Reidel, S.P., 1998, "Emplacement of Columbia River flood basalt": *Journal of Geophysical Research*, v. 103, no. B11, p. 27, 393-27410.

Schuster, J.E., compiler, 1994, *Geologic map of the Walla Walla 1:100,000 quadrangle*: Washington Division of Geology and Earth Resources Open File Report 94-3, 18 p.

Schuster, J.E., C.W. Gulick, S.P. Reidel, K.R. Fecht and Stephanie Zurenko, 1997, *Geologic map of Washington – southeast quadrant*: Washington Division of Geology and Earth Resources Geologic Map GM-45 (scale 1:250,000).

Smith, G.A., 1993, "Missoula flood dynamics and magnitudes inferred from sedimentology of slack-water deposits on the Columbia Plateau, Washington": *Geological Society of America Bulletin*, v. 105, p. 77-100.

Vallier, Tracy, 1998, *Islands and rapids: A geologic story of Hells Canyon*: Lewiston, Idaho, Confluence Press, 151 p.

Van Auken, Heidi, 1998, "The changing Walla Walla River: A 200 year perspective, with emphasis on inundation due to the construction of McNary Dam on the Columbia River": Walla Walla, Washington, Whitman College bachelor of arts thesis, 49 p.

Van Tassell, J., M. Ferns, V. McConnell and G.R. Smith, 2001, "The mid-Pliocene Imbler fish fossils, Grande Ronde Valley, Union County, Oregon, and the connection between Lake Idaho and the Columbia River": *Oregon Geology*, v. 63, no. 3, p. 77-84, 89-96.

Tolan, T.L. and S.P. Reidel, compilers, 1989, "Structure map of a portion of the Columbia River flood-basalt province," *in* S.P. Reidel and P.R. Hooper, eds., *Volcanism and tectonism in the Columbia River flood-basalt province*: Geological Society of America Special Paper 239, scale 1:580,000.

Waitt, R.B. Jr., 1980, "About forty last-glacial Lake Missoula jökulhlaups through southern Washington": *Journal of Geology*, v. 88, p. 653-679.

Walker, G.W., 1977, *Geologic map of Oregon east of the 121st meridian*: U.S. Geological Survey Miscellaneous Investigations Series Map I-902, scale 1:500,000.

Weis, P.L. and W.L. Newman, 1989, *The Channeled Scablands of eastern Washington – The geologic story of the Spokane Flood*: Cheney, Washington, Eastern Washington University Press, 25 p.

Williams, Hill, 2002, *The restless Northwest: A geological story*: Pullman, Washington, Washington State University Press, 176 p.

Wohl, Ellen, 2004, *Disconnected rivers: Linking rivers to landscapes*: New Haven, Connecticut, Yale University Press, 301 p.

Juniper tree just south of the Twin Sisters at Wallula Gap. (John Clement photo)

4

Biology:
Seasons in the Sun

Michael E. Denny

"When man continues to destroy nature, he saws off the very branch on which he sits since the rational protection of nature is at the same time the protection of mankind."

–Vinzenz Ziswiler, 1967, *Extinct and Vanishing Animals*

The habitat changes in space (basalt pinnacles and talus slopes) and time (winter and spring). (Bob Carson/Bob Baker photo)

Early Natural History

Before the introduction of cheatgrass, shad, Russian thistle (tumbleweed), carp, chukar, Russian wheat aphid, yellow sack spider, California quail, yellow star thistle, European starlings or Chinese ring-necked pheasants; back when native peoples and wildlife roamed the landscape, and native shrub-steppe (the living community of desert plants dominated by the many species of sagebrush, bunchgrasses and cryptobiotic soil crusts) dominated the entire area; back when the Columbia River was choked with salmon, whitefish and steelhead (many now listed under the Endangered Species Act) and California condors (now extirpated from the Pacific Northwest) fed on their spent carcasses; back when this great river flooded, and spotty riparian corridors grew along its braided shorelines; and back when great long sandbars crowded this river's waters, Wallula Gap was.

Populations of black-tailed jackrabbits (on the critical list), white-tailed jackrabbits (on the threatened list), and Washington ground squirrel (on the endangered list) thrived above the gap, as did sage grouse and Columbia sharp-tailed grouse (both extirpated from the region). Pronghorn antelope (extirpated from all of southeastern Washington), mountain lion, bighorn sheep and the occasional lynx (on the endangered list) wandered this area. Wapiti, mule deer and peregrine falcon were seldom seen, though present.

Many species of small vertebrates and invertebrates also thrived in this unique area, adapted to sudden and rapid habitat changes brought on by drought, fire or flood. The living skin of this region, the cryptobiotic soil crust that sealed the moisture in and held the thin topsoils in place, was intact. This region saw few

This cryptobiotic soil crust has tiny flowers in the spring. Elsewhere at Wallula Gap these crusts are dominated by mosses. They may also have lichens and algae. Biological soil crusts are important for stability, fertility and moisture retention. Disruption of the crust by boots, hooves and vehicles may increase erosion and invasion by weeds. (Mike Denny photo)

Sunset over the mouth of the Walla Walla River. Behind the old and new highway bridges the Walla Walla River is building a delta in the resevoir of the Columbia River. (Kathryn Farrell photo)

if any introductions of plants, birds or mammals until the dawn of the 19th century, when modern horses and other livestock started to arrive in the Columbia Basin. As trade routes and human numbers began to increase, so did intentional and unintended introductions of non-native fish, plants, birds and mammals. Diseases unknown until the 1800s also crept into the gap and often proved too much for native humans and animals alike.

Walla Walla River Delta

In southwestern Walla Walla County, Washington, to the northeast of Wallula Gap, at the confluence of the Walla Walla and Columbia rivers, a delta splays out into the Columbia River more than a half mile to the north and northwest as each successive flood event in the Walla Walla River drainage deposits its layer of silt. This vitally important river delta has not always been composed of mud and silts. Before massive wheat farms and the loss of native grass prairie, before the encroachment of farms onto the rich-soiled uplands of the northern Blue Mountains, before the loss of critical riparian corridors along creeks and streams, this delta was mostly river cobble, sand and clear, cold water.

In our age, flood events occur from time to time on the western face of the Blue Mountains. Rapidly melting snow or heavy rains rush down off the steep farmed slopes, pulling topsoils into the creeks and rivers. These soil-saturated waters rip down the nowchannelized riverbeds of the Touchet and Walla Walla rivers, and as the speed of the flood slackens, suspended particles begin to drop out of the water column. Once the floodwaters reach the slack water pool of Lake Wallula, the current slows and spreads out across the delta, depositing yet another layer of topsoil.

These constant infusions of fresh silt and organic matter make this delta area a great magnet for resident and migrant birds. This slice of mud and the associated riparian cover is vital as a rest stop for migrating species of shorebirds and dozens of species of Neotropical songbirds. After the big floods of 1996 and 1997 in the Walla Walla River drainage, the delta expanded by 45 percent, or more than a quarter mile farther out into the Columbia River and Lake Wallula, creating one of the premier resting and feeding areas along the interior Pacific Flyway for shorebirds and waterfowl. In August,

up to 2,000 western sandpipers will land on this delta in a single morning after an all-night flight out of Canada. These 1.2-ounce birds land here to rest, preen, feed and rebuild badly needed energy reserves for the next night flight south into the Great Basin and on down into Central and South America. Up to 16 species of shorebirds depend on this important site, bringing with them small numbers of peregrine falcons that pick off the injured, weak and old, maintaining a strong, vigorous gene pool for the future.

Wind

The basalt rims that form the gap overlook the river that exposed them, allowing numerous species of native and introduced plants and animals a place to live a season at a time. The stricture of the gap

View west up the lower Walla Walla River. Natural levees separate two ponds from the river. Every year the delta grows farther out into the reservoir. (Bob Carson photo)

Wallula Gap from the north. Prominent in the center is the delta of the Walla Walla River, deposited since McNary Dam blocked the Columbia River in the mid-1950s. (Bob Carson photo)

and the sudden rise of the Horse Heaven Hills from the flat, lower Columbia Basin create a unique set of resulting winds, an important component of Wallula Gap. These winds may suddenly reach 35 to 50-plus mph on the approach of a cold front or summer storm and are often unique to the gap; a few miles away there may be just a breeze. During periods of migration, the wind out of the gap forces thousands of migrating birds to hold up on the Walla Walla River delta to the northeast. In the direct path of these powerful winds, this delta area provides outstanding cover to sheltering birds. The winds have also dispersed many introduced plants at this westward bend of the river. Millions of small spiders ride great, long strands of silken gossamer through the late summer afternoon winds to their future territories.

Fire

Fire has been a natural, integral agent of change within the system of the gap. Fires burned mosaic patterns through the sagebrush and rabbitbrush along the walls of the gap, allowing for replacement of mature plants with young ones, leaving islands of mature stands as seed sources. Dense stands of mature sagebrush were burned off, opening up areas and allowing for colonization by a wide variety of native forbs and grasses. The native bunchgrasses and rabbitbrush were revitalized by these rapid, spotty fires, often putting out new growth in as little as five weeks. The sage and western junipers were

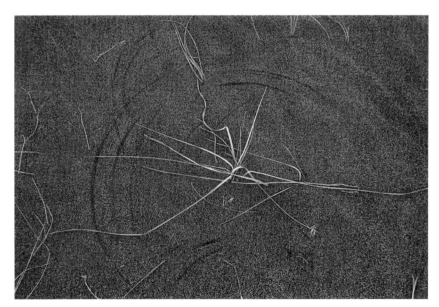

Wind pushes the grass around, making circles in the sand. (Dianne Kornberg photo)

Fire is a common occurrence in the grasses. Often started as trains pass, winds quickly spread the fire for miles along the sides of Wallula Gap. Here on July 29, 2007, fire burns behind a train on the west side of the gap. (Bob Carson photo)

Clockwise, from top left: Sagebrush. (John Clement photo) Sagebrush and sand dunes east of the Twin Sisters. This Arnold Photo was hand colored by Mrs. Arnold. (Fred L. Mitchell Collection) Orange globe mallow, a native flower. (Mike Denny photo) Phacelia flowers spring up among the snags of burned sage. (Clare Carson photo)

killed, removing these plants and their dominating heavy canopies for years to come. These fires appeared when the native grasses and forbs had dried out near the middle of July and on into late October, allowing for a natural progression of plant replacement over time with mature sage and junipers being the climax of the shrub-steppe community. These burns were set by native tribes or were caused by lightning strikes at unknown intervals across time. Prior to the 20th century, the effects of fire within the gap were short-term and mitigated by natural, native plant regeneration – always building toward a climax sage community (vascular plant community with mature sage, rabbitbrush, bitterbrush, bunchgrass and native forbs; key indicators are western juniper and cryptobiotic soil crust). Since the early 20th century and the unchecked spread of non-native weeds such as cheatgrass, Russian thistle, tumble mustard and yellow

Tumble mustard (exotic) beside willow (native). (Dianne Kornberg photo)

star thistle, natural fire has had a wholly unnatural impact.

These Asian invasive weeds have created circumstances that have all but obliterated the natural response to fire by native plants throughout the gap. Cheatgrass grows dense and fast, instantly draining nutrients weeks before any native grasses or forbs come out of dormancy. By the end of March, it is often more than half grown and awaiting the warmer weather of April to bloom and produce seed. By the end of May, this bromegrass is drying out and has already dropped its seeds as our native grasses are just starting to green and bloom. By the fourth week of May it is dry, and this huge fuel load is ready to burn. The tumble mustards and Russian thistle grow large and fast and pack in tightly between the remaining native sage and rabbitbrush. By the first week of June, if a fire ignites, it burns hot, rapidly and far, leaving nothing in its wake. It bakes the surface of the ground, killing whatever seedbed is present except for the cheatgrass seed, which has burrowed deeply due to its design.

After a fire of this nature, a fire regime is established, and most native plants are lost, as no immediate seed sources remain. Cheatgrass, tumble mustards and yellow star thistle will colonize the newly fire-cleared areas, which will burn, on average, every three to five years. These burns also demolish the native cryptobiotic soil crust so valuable for holding soil moisture and thin topsoils in place. This new fire regime changes all the usage patterns of the birds, reptiles and mammals that utilize these areas, and the full extent of the damage is still being monitored.

Once these invasive weeds establish themselves, soil, native wildlife cover and forage are lost. With this loss, many sage-obligate species of birds and mammals are no longer sustained in these areas. The western juniper is now confined to Juniper Canyon along with several species of native forbs. Juniper trees cannot withstand even the coolest-burning fire. Only with great effort will these remaining native plant communities be maintained and protected from any future fires. Today's devastating premature fires in the gap are caused by thoughtless smokers, lightning strikes, sparking trains and operating farm machinery during extremely hot weather.

Russian Olive

During the last years of the 19th century, the Russian olive was introduced from Asia as a tree species that could withstand dry winds, long, cold winters and drought. This tree would help eliminate surface waters and wetlands as the Columbia Basin was settled. Right on through the 1970s, this tough tree was planted everywhere in the region along the Columbia River providing a solution to shallow water tables and giving cover to man and beast alike. This invasive tree species has been well-established for more than 100 years, and many native birds and mammals have become dependent on this plant for winter survival and cover.

In the early 1990s it was decided that this invasive species should be removed from public lands, regardless of the impact to native wildlife. Reasons cited were the loss of native willows, the increased nesting of black-billed magpies, the plant's invasiveness and its uncontrolled spread into all wetlands. This species has withstood state and federal government's attempts at removal by cutting, spraying and burning. Dense stands of these gray-green-foliaged thorny trees are sprinkled throughout the gap along the Columbia River. The dense canopy, copious berry production and outstanding winter thermal cover of this tree have endeared it to many birds and

Russian olive trees are an exotic species on which many native animals have become dependent. (Mike Denny photos)

mammals throughout the lower Columbia Basin.

One example of a created dependency is the case of the yellow-rumped warbler, which is a common nesting species high in the Blue Mountains, the Cascades and the Selkirks. This insectivore passes along the shores of the Columbia River in great numbers during spring and fall migration. Flocks of thousands arrive in the basin in early September and swarm into the Russian olive groves to feast on the huge insect numbers associated with these trees. As the fall season turns to winter, this warbler species will hold up in the Russian olives, feeding on insect egg masses hidden in the soft tissues of the olive-like berries. During many winters large numbers of these warblers will winter in these dense stands along with wood ducks, long-eared owls, black-billed magpies, evening grosbeaks, orange-crowned warblers, hermit thrushes, varied thrushes, American robins, Bewick's wrens, cedar waxwings, winter wrens, Bohemian waxwings, European starlings and northern saw-whet owls, to name a few. You can get close views of this interesting tree at Sand Station Recreation Area, Hat Rock State Park and Madame Dorion Park near the Walla Walla River delta. Watch out for the Russian olive's long boot-piercing thorns.

Wallula Gap's Native Mollusks

The Columbia River in Wallula Gap hosts three, known native species of freshwater mussels: margaritifers (western pearlshell), the gonidea (western ridged mussel) and the anodonta or floater mussel. These long-lived (up to 100 years and beyond) native animals are of vital importance to the Snake and Columbia River systems and many of their tributaries. The Columbia River at Wallula Gap was once a clear, cold, flowing river that moved west between large, broad sandbars and a great sandy delta area. In this system these native mussels lived and reproduced in great numbers, if today's populations in undammed tributaries are any indication.

Each of these three species of mussels has adopted different strategies for survival. The western pearlshell mussel is colonial and forms large, dense beds of thousands of animals knitted together by strong bissell threads, forming a safety net. The Oregon floater mussel is solitary and will burrow down into gravel substrates with only its siphon exposed. The western ridged mussel will burrow into the roots of emergent vegetation or beside large boulders and rocks, where it too lives a solitary life. Each of these mussel species lives by a common thread, its complete dependency on dace or salmonid fish for success in reproductive cycles. These mussels produce a larval stage called a glochidia (pronounced glaw-kiddy-a). This minute,

Western pearlshell, a freshwater mussel. (Bob Carson photo)

multisharp-toothed larval form is then expelled into the water column, but not before the parent mussel produces a lure to attract dace and salmonid fish species into close range. These lures are fish-species specific and unique in shape and color to each mussel species.

One species of mussel produces a 4-foot-long clear gelatinous strand with a 3.5-inch-long, white willow-leaf-shaped opaque lure on the end; this lure was just discovered in the mid-1990s. The lure flaps in the current, attracting fish to within range of the expelled glochidia that are then pulled into and across the gills by the fish in the act of breathing. This blood-rich region is now parasitized as the glochidia attach to the gills and connect to the host's blood supply. The fish now moves up or downstream with its load of growing young mussels. After a time, these small mussels drop off the fish gills and are carried down onto the river bottom where they burrow and start their lives as filter feeders, providing an important service to the life of the host river. These animals at maturity can filter upward of 10 to 12 gallons of water per day per mussel.

From the mid-1920s on, the silt load in the Columbia River has only increased, covering up many healthy populations of native mussels during flood events. With the construction of McNary Dam, the river's ability to flush silts away was effectively compromised, and the health of the native mussel population remains unknown. The introduction of non-native fish and mollusks, such as the Asian clam, may have severely damaged the populations of native bivalves (clams and mussels). There are also many native species of gastropods (aquatic snails) that live within the gap, all with unique life histories. Many western species of mollusks have yet to be inventoried or even documented.

Spring

Dashing, diving, cutting and slicing, a dozen white-throated swifts rip through the warming air high above Wallula Gap and the great basalt faces in which they nest. These 1.1-ounce, 6.75-inch-long Neotropic migrants arrive the third week of March on rigid, dark, scimitar-shaped wings. Their chittering calls echo off the walls announcing yet another season of renewed life in the gap. With gape ajar, these swifts slam into flying insects at speeds greater than 50 mph as they hunt the rising thermals of the advancing day.

Rosy balsamroot and northern wyethia along with the bunchgrasses, gray rabbitbrush, sagebrush and stonecrops abandon dormancy and spring to life on the slopes and ridges above the river.

Colorful wildflowers hide in the green grasses of spring. The basalt cliff has prominent vertical fractures. (Bob Baker photo)

Mule deer, porcupine, the locally rare bighorn sheep, rabbits and rodents relish the new, green growth on the still-moist, north-facing slopes of the gap. With a series of sweet descending notes, a canyon wren adds to the season's notice of ownership. These white-breasted, white-speckled, rufous-bodied native wrens bring life to the dead basalt. As they search for spiders and insects, the wrens move under and around the lava rims, in and out of numerous cracks and holes in this ancient rock. An adult prairie falcon perches halfway up a weathered, dark, pockmarked basalt face spattered with expanding, concentric patches of bright yellow, green and orange lichens. Intent on a pair of common ravens drifting west above the blue river, the falcon shifts its weight, utters a strident scream and departs its white-spattered perch on rapid, powerful, shallow wing beats. The ravens tuck their black, heavy wings and cough, rasp and roll as they mentally outdistance the falcon in their search for the perfect nest site along one of the many rims. These *corvids* (bird family including ravens, jays, crows and magpies) lay claim to all that lives in this gap as sustenance for their survival. All the living and the dead are inspected and noted in memories as deep as these birds are black.

Far below, a Say's phoebe sits atop a small island of sagebrush just where a steep talus slope collides with a basalt wall. He has been in the area since mid-February, having spent most of the winter in the desert southwest. This flycatcher easily survives the last, few frosty mornings as he feeds on the numerous midges and flies that rise with midday warmth. Giving his *"phee-wee"* call, this bird sets out to attract a mate and establish a defensible territory among the basalt walls of the gap. When he is successful in luring a female into his territory, they will build a tight-cupped nest within a crack or cavity.

By March the sun reaches into and warms the myriad cracks and fissures in the cold basalt of the southeastern wall of the gap. Butterflies awake from hibernation and work their way into the direct rays of the sun. With wings out flat to soak up the energy and warmth, the *brush-foots,* such as morning cloak, Milbert's tortoiseshell, California tortoiseshell and anglewings, are soon joined by the first emerging desert marbles – bringing early color to this awakening landscape.

With sharp *"deedet-deedet"* calls coming from several directions along the lower rims just above an area of fractured basalt, the rock wrens alert the community in the gap to a pair of retreating northern rough-legged hawks. This pair of raptors spent the winter in the lower Columbia Basin feeding on voles and pocket gophers. With the increase in daylight, these hawks are catching a thermal to head north to the Arctic tundra, where they will nest on the ground during that region's short summer.

With loud chatter and raucous calls three black-billed magpies harass a roosting great horned owl wedged into a fold in the ancient magma. A fourth picks at the remnants of the owl's last kill – a cottontail rabbit lying bare-boned and bloody about 60 feet below on a strip of sprouting bunchgrass. The rabbit's severed tail lies like a fur ball under a sage bush, slowly pushed side to side by a light morning breeze, as ants remove the last soft tissues from around the tailbones. A scant 150 feet up, on an old raven's nest situated just behind several jutting fingers of basalt, the owl's larger mate sits atop three, white downy chicks sequentially hatched two days apart. She and her young go unnoticed by the marauding magpies, although regurgitated pellets, droppings, bits of fur and bone are sprinkled down the steep talus slope to the rocks below.

The skin of this desert is the cryptobiotic soil crust comprised of native ground lichens, mosses, bryophytes, bacteria and algae. These crust communities appear to inhibit the penetration and germination of non-native grasses like cheatgrass and help retain badly needed topsoils and soil moisture. However, once the crust is trampled or broken up, the site is open to infestation by invasive weeds, loss of moisture and thinning of soils by wind erosion. When these crust communities are demolished, they take decades to reestablish and then only if topsoils are still intact. All the steep ground sloping down to and below the basalt rims looks terraced with a latticework of game trails established millennia ago, then widened and compacted by many generations of sheep and cattle over the last century. Few native plants survive along these paths, as cheatgrass and tumble mustard dominate with the cryptobiotic soil crust hammered out of existence by countless hooves.

By mid-March the air above and below the gap is alive with hundreds of swallows returning from Central and South America for the breeding season. Violet-green, cliff and a few tree and barn swallows now cut and dive after flying insects out over the great river. The earliest migrants, the violet-green swallows, are secretive cavity nesters that seek the deep cracks of the basalt rims. Cliff swallows, on the other hand, are colonial nesters that plaster their round ball-shaped, mud-daubed nests side by side on some slight overhang. These colonies are a cacophony of constant grinding, chirping and alarms to one degree or another. Everything these birds do is done en masse: clouds of swallows arrive, and clouds depart by the hundreds as they gather at puddles. With pulsating, twitching wings extended high above their backs, they fill their beaks with cool wet mud to return to the forming colony.

With a series of loud "*cur-lew*" calls, a long-billed curlew announces the species' arrival on the uplands above the gap. These chicken-sized shorebirds winter along the eastern Pacific Coast from Tokeland, Washington, south to the central Baja California coast. Curlews arrive with a flurry of chases, loud calling and amazing display flights in early March. These ground nesters lay four, large, mottled eggs in a loose-grass bowl. Always on the lookout for coyotes, ravens, rodents and northern harriers, these dedicated birds spend the nesting season providing grasshoppers for and protecting their precocious young. During the breeding season, pairs and family groups fly down to the Walla Walla River delta to drink and bathe in the early evening hours. This species will vanish from above the gap by the heat of mid-July and retreat to cooler beaches and estuaries of the coast in the never-ending search for food.

As surface soils warm, multitudes of ants appear and launch into the season's work of maintaining untold numbers of colonies. With no time off in the foreseeable future, these ants proceed to collect the detritus that sustains them through the coming seasons, often carrying loads up to 10 times their size and five times their weight as they scour this windblown land for sustenance. Many different species of ants inhabit this desert gap area as they work to maintain and defend their queens and colonies. These ant species will battle over turf, harvest crops, feed young and avoid predators.

With a few, rapid flips of its burnished-copper-colored, cowbell-shaped head and horizontal, pincer-like mandibles, the ant lion larvae removes grains of fine sand from its funnel-shaped trap. This quarter-inch-long insect lies buried at the bottom of its trap, its pincers set ajar, awaiting the next hapless ant to slide down into its trap. Soft bodied and hard headed, these master predators lie motionless until an ant alters its travel to investigate the perfect funnel. Perhaps lured by chemical pheromones emitted by the ant lion, the ant proceeds slowly down into the trap when suddenly all six legs slip in the fine sand, and the ant loses traction. Tumbling out of control it rolls down, then stops with its legs spread wide and slowly starts to climb up the sides of the trap. The ant lion begins rapidly flipping the fine sand out from under the creeping ant, pulling it ever closer to the ant lion's hard-wired jaws. The ant attempts to speed up the funnel wall, but with an instant snap the ant lion grasps the ant between its long mandibles, and with its front pair of paddle-like legs, it swims back under the sand, pulling down its prey. Piercing the ant exoskeleton with sharp mouth parts, this small hunter now sucks all the fluid from the ant's body. Sometime later, long after the ant's last twitch of life, the ant lion pushes the lifeless form back to the center of the funnel and with a flip of its head sends the dried body up and out of the trap to be carried away by the wind or another ant. Ant lions and their funnel traps may be found along the base of basalt rims in powder-dry soil and sand.

Undetected, save for a crouching horned lark, the largest buteo in North America drifts low over the gap. Held aloft on a 56-inch wingspan, the ferruginous hawk searches with its great, yellow eyes for ground squirrels, pocket gophers and young marmots along the crest of the basalt rim. With the morning sun reflecting off its russet scapulars and great, white tail, this regal raptor lands on a rise near several pocket gopher mounds. Facing the gap with its pure-white breast and belly framed by its rust-feathered leggings, the huge hawk watches for movement. Pressed by man on every side, this species is in sharp decline locally and deserves every effort to conserve the habitat it requires.

At the base of a basalt cliff far below, a lone Pacific gopher snake works its cold, stiff way into the life-sustaining warmth of the morning sun. This beautiful serpent, splashed with warm tans and browns, reaches 45 inches in length. Although harmless, this snake mimics the greatly feared western rattlesnake by vibrating its long, sharp tail in dead grass and plant litter, causing some to believe it deserves to die. An integral part of the ecology of the gap, this snake consumes many species of rodents, and contrary to popular belief, it does not feed on rattlesnakes. In fact, gopher snakes frequently den with western rattlesnakes under talus slopes within the gap.

The northwestern wall of the gap soaks up the heat of the southern sun all winter, and by early March many species of insects and plants are well ahead of those same species clinging to the cooler,

Wallula Gap at sunrise, seen from the town of Wallula. The dry basalt cliffs contrast with the lush vegetation by Lake Wallula. (Kathryn Farrell photo)

damper, north-facing shaded rim. The advancing summer heat will soon draw moisture away from both sides of the gap, leaving only small, isolated seeps to provide badly needed water during the long, hot desert summer. In the dry season the wildlife of the gap risk instant death by crossing U.S. Highway 730 and the railroad tracks as they try to reach the riprapped shore of the Columbia and its life-giving waters. Many birds, insects and animals are crushed along these transportation routes by drivers ignorant of their existence.

A loud, caustic, repeated "*ker-ruck*" splashes across the gap as a pair of chukars roam up and over the jagged, fractured lava in search of fresh, green sprouts of cheatgrass. Native to the steppes of Central Asia, this beautiful partridge arrived with help from the state fish and game agencies from both sides of the gap, which hoped to bolster the upland game bird hunt. The chukars are far from the only non-native bird species in the gap. With a series of deep soft "*whoo-oo-uh*" calls, dozens of introduced feral pigeons or rock pigeons compete for females and nest sites in the basalt cliffs along the entire gap. This multicolored species abounds in the gap, sustained by spilt grain and other plant seeds. They coo and perform outstanding aerial maneuvers as they present an important prey base for several species of native raptors. Producing nerve-splitting screeching, grinding, chipping and mimicking native bird species' calls, introduced European starlings also move into the gap to inspect every hole, crack or cavity for potential nest sites. With intelligence, these interlopers dominate many breeding sites starting in late March, and native cavity-nesting bird species are often outcompeted, and their populations suffer as starlings appropriate most of the choice cavities.

Native sunflowers are much smaller than cultivated sunflowers. (Bob Carson photo)

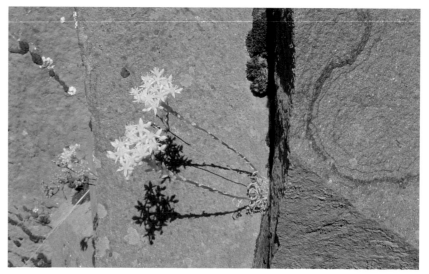

Stonecrop and basalt columns. (Mike Denny photo)

Large numbers of composite flowers now come into bloom along with phlox, astragalus, onions and violets, to name a few. The short, intense growing season in the gap requires a near rapacious fervor by all species preparing to survive the approaching heat of summer.

Slowly crawling and chewing their way through the patches of vivid, green plants are numbers of alert yellow-bellied marmots. Unhurried, they work their way over and around the basalt rocks in search of new sprouts, tender stems, bulbs and roots. These large rodents first appear during the early days of February to capitalize on emerging, green shoots of grass. Pulled out of hibernation by warmer late winter days and a hunger that must be answered, these mammals venture out in hopes of dense, green pastures on which to feed. With a sudden, stentorian call, a lookout warns of a golden eagle approaching as the marmots, fat bodied and short legged, bolt for the safety of their hibernacula and burrows under basalt boulders.

The golden eagle spins lazy circles on long, broad wings out over the gap, staying clear of the great rows of wind turbines to the east and west. These birds no longer nest within the gap and only infrequently hunt the area for its marmots, fawns, pup coyotes, jackrabbits and cottontail rabbits. Their numbers were greatly reduced during long decades of sheepherding in the gap. Now protected, this raptor has never moved back into the area as a breeder.

Spring evenings bring many seldom-seen animals into view as the warming earth awakens them. Burrowing amphibians are now drawn to the surface in search of mates and standing pools of precious water in which to deposit their eggs. Tiger salamanders, Great Basin spadefoot toads and the range-limited Woodhouse's toad all head for water in March and April. After long nights of enthusiastic sex and egg laying, these porous-skinned animals burrow back into the soils of the gap to escape the desiccative rays of the summer sun.

Summer Migration Through the Gap

The first bird species giving any hint of a post-breeding migration materialize at the northeast end of the gap on the Walla Walla River delta during the last week of June in the form of a few adult greater and lesser yellowlegs along with small numbers of adult western sandpipers. Arriving from breeding grounds far to the north on the Arctic tundra en route to Central and South American coastlines,

Western sandpiper. (Bob Baker photo)

these shorebirds pause to rebuild much-needed body fat. Loafing and foraging on the invertebrate-rich mudflats of this delta, these Neotropic migrants are soon joined by thousands of sand martins or bank swallows that have completed their nesting cycle in countless cut bank burrow colonies in the Columbia Basin. Like the sandpipers, they are being pulled to the south in the middle of a long, hot summer. Massing on the delta by the thousands in preparation for long flights down into the Middle Americas, these 0.47-ounce swallows take advantage of the millions of hatching midges, flies and leafhoppers that swarm into the warm air above the delta and its mudflats. On crescent-shaped wings, this circumpolar swallow species slices through the insect-choked air just above the humid mud, and with audible pops they ingest one flying insect after another.

With the rising heat of early July, insect numbers are at their apex just in time for the first major movements of post-breeding adult swallows and shorebirds. These birds follow the Columbia River migration corridor south out of Canada. Upon arriving at the Walla Walla River delta and the great westward bend of the Columbia River into the gap, species' specific choices are made whether to migrate south away from the Columbia or west through the gap and along the great river, then south down along the eastern face of the Cascade Mountains, or out to the Pacific Ocean and south along the coast. Some species bid farewell to the Columbia at Wallula Gap, heading south overland across the Blue Mountains and on into the Great Basin and its invertebrate-rich saline lakes.

For shorebirds, migration begins at dusk, as both mixed-species flocks and homogeneous groups rise through the columns of dancing midges and caddis flies. With stiff, rapid flight, these small birds wing their way into the warm night. Uttering constant location peeps and calls, these Arctic nesters ensure the groups' cohesiveness as they blast south under the stars to the next appointed rest stop far to the south of the gap. These birds' night movements and inclement weather often slam them into unseen manmade obstacles such as wind turbines and television, radio, cell phone and microwave towers and their guy lines. High-tension power lines also kill and injure many night migrants. Bird migration has been complicated immeasurably in this age of great power lines, high towers, lights, automobiles, fences and now wind turbines across ancient migration paths. We humans have become increasingly difficult to live with.

By early July the heat index has climbed into the mid-90s or higher, and southward migration has slowed to a dull roar with a few new species appearing weekly on the delta. The end of the third week of July brings many changes to the northeastern gap as the force of bird migration floods into this area. The adult sandpipers dominate this portion of early migration, having abandoned their precocial young out on the Arctic tundra and flown south, taking leisurely hops from one feeding site to the next. However, these sites are becoming fewer and farther apart, which makes the Walla Walla River delta all the more vital for shorebird migration. By early August least, western, solitary and spotted sandpipers have all arrived, and the western sandpipers number into the thousands. The gap from Port Kelley west to Sand Station is now a major feeding site for Caspian terns, western grebes, double-crested cormorants and thousands of California and ring-billed gulls. Even a few summering, nonbreeding common loons feed here. During the heat of midsummer, other species of birds also start to shift locations and to wander, leaving established nest sites. Post-breeding wandering by adult passerines (songbirds) ebbs and flows through the gap.

A Walla Walla River Delta Carp

With an odd, side-to-side gait through the shallow skin of warm, slightly opaque water that covers some of the delta on hot summer afternoons, a lone American white pelican is drawn to a midsized carp. The fish is stranded in one of the numerous carp wallows carved out of the soft substrate of the delta it feeds in during high pool conditions created by McNary Dam. Caught in this 10- to 15-inch deep, 3- to 9-foot wide oval pool out in the delta mudflats, this destructive, introduced fish sucks air from the surface as the water temperature of its prison climbs.

The carp's splashing and surface sucking has attracted the opportunistic pelican. Several subadult California gulls shadow the larger bird in hopes of a payoff in fresh carp. This heavy-scaled, bony fish now sees a short future, and in a vain attempt to escape its fate, races around in the tight confines of the small pool, muddying the water. Coming to a sudden stop in the clouded pool, the carp sits still as the pelican probes, open-billed. Suddenly, the carp is contacted and it shoots up and out of the thick, brown water onto the exposed mud of the flats, where it flops and is instantly covered with heavy dark mud. With an extended neck and a sideways grasp, the pelican quickly envelops the soiled, thrashing carp in the large, soft, yellow-orange skinned pouch of its lower mandible. The gulls mount a halfhearted rush at the pelican in an attempt to intimidate this large piscivorous bird out of its catch. The pelican now rejects the mud-covered fish, and with its bill open, allows it to slide onto the warm, sun-drenched mud to the mercy of the gulls.

Moving along the bottom like huge herds of cattle foraging on pasture are large schools of these bottom feeders, the most destructive, introduced fish species in the waters of the gap. The carp root around on the bottom by the hundreds of thousands, pushing great, billowing plumes of silt into the water column, blocking out vital light and limiting the plant growth on which so many native species of insects, fish and birds depend. Introduced from Europe during the 19th century by people who enjoyed its distinctive earthy flavor, this heavy-boned fish rapidly spread unchecked into any slow-flowing warm waters. Carp find it very difficult to survive rapid flow, cold water, sand and cobble substrate streams and rivers. But the warm water pool behind McNary Dam is ready-made to shelter and grow huge numbers of these mud-billowing fish.

In attempts to control carp, state and federal land managers have used several waterborne poisons that block the uptake of oxygen by the gills to suffocate the fish. Unfortunately these poisons kill not only carp but also any larval and neotenic (sexually mature aquatic) native salamanders, all frog and toad tadpoles, and all native fish that might be in the area. Out on the Walla Walla River delta mudflats during the weekly high pool, carp swarm out over the flats and proceed to root out deep holes as they forage for red worms and sprouting seeds. In April and May this species spawns in vast numbers over the mud of the delta during high pool periods.

Cover in Time of Summer Storm

Wallula Gap is a desert, and rain events are rare during the summer months. But once a month or so, southward bird movements are both aided and halted by prevailing storm patterns that push up from the southwest and force many species of birds in transit to seek cover from the high winds of the gap. The thin margin of willow and introduced false indigo along the immediate shoreline of the Columbia often provide this shelter on a short-term basis. The large, luxuriant foliage of the introduced Russian olive tree acts as a magnet during these storm events and provides outstanding protection from sudden rain and wind. Because there are very few native black cottonwoods left along the shorelines of the gap, migrating and nesting birds utilize the few remaining river birch, alder and Russian olive trees for cover.

Summer Evening

On a warm, late summer evening, after the sun falls behind the

Horse Heaven Hills to the west, and a long twilight passes across the sky, several common nighthawks take to the heavens. These crepuscular birds dip and drop, only to rise on stiff boomerang wings in pursuit of some hapless insect. Uttering their *"preeent"* call, they slip through the air, gape ajar, hunting into the leading edge of the night.

The fading light lures bats from the basalt rims to the creeping river's surface. In search of prey they twist, flutter and rock on thin membranes of skin. Both resident and migratory bats such as big browns, hoary and silver-haired bats sally forth in search of rising columns of hatching midges, mayflies and caddis flies, beetles and moths. The surface of the Columbia River is burnished in fading gold, violet and pink as the last of the gulls, terns and cormorants return upstream to the islands off the Walla Walla River delta to roost and await a new day. The last calls of the chukar bounce off

Sunset over Lake Wallula. (Bob Carson photo)

the great walls of the gap as barn and great horned owls vacate their day roosts in cracks and holes to plunge into the night in search of rodents, rabbits, snakes and birds.

A lone spotted night snake works its way toward the surface of one of the steep talus slopes. Out from under the protective rock, its forked tongue sniffs the light breeze for a hint of what lies ahead in this desert dusk. When this mildly venomous, back-fanged serpent finds a warm rock on the surface of which to crawl, it soon detects prey in the vicinity and slides away in search of it. This nocturnal snake feeds on small lizards, insects and baby rodents it detects by sniffing the air with its sensitive tongue.

Rubbing and wiping its face and long, silky whiskers, a bushy-tailed woodrat sits atop a white-capped, ridged basalt boulder as it pulls and presses with clawed digits those hairs that lie out of place. This midsized rodent perches on a territorial marking post stained by urea from successive generations of woodrats claiming this territory. The rat, now finished primping, also adds its urine to this historic deposit and drops down onto a neighboring rock and begins the never-ending search for food and more stuff to drag back to its already-sizable stash of sticks, bones, bright plastics and shiny metals, hence the nickname "pack rat." Each and every great find it makes supports its claim to be the "garage sale" rodent of the gap.

Insect numbers decline up in the basalt rims of the gap as the fierce summer sun sucks away any moisture. After 100-plus degree days, only the night brings relief and sustains the lives of those that can somehow escape under rocks, into cavities or down to the river.

Behind McNary Dam, native fish try to survive the warm slack water and the large numbers of introduced, highly predatory fish such as largemouth bass, black crappie, the walleye pike, yellow perch and smallmouth bass, to name a few. The native squawfish, recently renamed the northern pikeminnow, was part of the natural flow of life in these waters long before the dams. Yet this fish species is blamed for unmitigated consumption of salmon and steelhead smolt. A bounty offered by the state to reduce its population tempts many fishermen to collect welfare at the expense of a native fish species.

Other native animals live along the river, and during the warm summer evenings they come into view. Muskrat, beaver, river otter, mink and striped skunks all utilize the cavities created by the large boulders laid as riprap for miles along the shores of the gap. There are few areas with natural shoreline or emergent vegetation left in the gap. Only the Walla Walla River delta presents this required habitat at the northeastern maw of the gap. The now-sluggish waters of this great river push west towards the retreating day as they pass through Wallula Gap.

Autumn

The approach of fall is subtle in the gap. The shriveling heat of summer hangs on well into late September, only relenting as the sun drifts off to the south and daylight shortens. By now the gap is stone dry with most plants dead, desiccated or dormant, save for the sage, rabbitbrush, western junipers and bitterbrush. Very little water is now found away from the great river. As thirst must be quenched, many animals along the southeast flank chance crossing the highway and, along both sides of the river, the busy rail lines. Many do not make it and become food for the scavengers: the coyotes, ravens, insects and magpies.

With the soft sound of stiff scales sliding over sand, a western rattlesnake slowly moves over the dry bed of a seasonal stream with its rattles held off the hot sand as it strives to reach the broken shade of a low sage, out of sight of a passing red-tailed hawk on patrol high above the basalt rims. As an ambush hunter, the western rattlesnake is eminently suited for life in the harsh climate of the gap. Normally nocturnal, these reptiles are found in good numbers along the southeast flank of the gap, and during early fall they prey on rodents to build up needed body fat for winter hibernation in a den with 15 to 20 other "rattlers." Rattlesnakes may only take as many as two to five rodents, depending on the year. Their name comes from the series of interlocking modified scales or keratin buttons at the end of the tail that the snake uses to warn larger animals of its presence. These buttons are formed as the snake grows and sheds its skin. Some individuals may shed their skin two or three times a

year, dispelling the myth that one can tell the age of a rattlesnake by the number of rattles on the tail. The only rattlesnake species in the Pacific Northwest, it is also the area's only venomous reptile of any consequence. Once this snake is detected, it should be avoided and left alone. This native reptile is part of the delicate living fabric of Wallula Gap.

The first shorebirds arrive from the Arctic the third week of June, adult birds that feed and loaf on the Walla Walla River delta as long as the mudflats are exposed. By the end of July the juveniles are arriving, with peak numbers of shorebirds by mid-August. These birds are frequently forced off the delta prematurely on the weekends throughout the migration period as the waters of Lake Wallula rise so that the needs of boaters, personal watercraft users and electrical power can be met. Other migrants arrive in the gap at this time as well. Songbirds such as black-headed grosbeaks, western tanagers,

View north from the east shore of Lake Wallula. (Mike Denny photo)

Western rattlesnake. (John Clement photo)

white-crowned sparrows, Wilson's warblers and willow flycatchers pass through in large numbers, utilizing the dense shoreline's woody shrubs and trees. These nocturnal migrants are part of the massive movement of birds working their way through the gap headed south, deep into Central and South America.

On rocking, stiff black wings, hundreds of Vaux's swifts blast south only meters above the ground as they twitter and call after rising from a patch of willows and cottonwood near the great river bend where they roosted the evening before. This species is a true Neotropic migrant that breeds in a few chimneys and commonly in large, hollow standing trees and snags throughout the Cascades and Blue Mountains. Rapid fliers like these swifts require constant fuel in the form of unlimited insects. Since the air temperatures keep bugs aloft, migrating flocks of these birds constantly feed as they move south away from the gap for a season.

At twilight during the warm evenings of early September, at the height of nocturnal songbird migration, millions of moths boil up over the Horse Heaven Hills in clouds as dense as dust storms, a mass movement south away from death and approaching winter. These flights contain species as diverse as loupers, sphinx and silks, to note a few. Just as large schools of fish or herds of ungulates are shadowed by predators, so are these clouds of moths. Cutting erratically in, about and through these masses of insects are numbers of migrating bats.

Also on the lookout for a chance to feed, coyotes patrol the entire gap. These master survivors have endured constant assault from humans in every form conceivable, yet their populations persist and flourish. Being a generalist helps this species survive: They will eat plants, road kills, insects, reptiles, fish and litter thrown out by the thoughtless. In the fall many of the year's offspring are out on their own, attempting to carve out a territory, stave off hunger and greet the next year's spring.

In the fall, the gray rabbitbrush bursts into brilliant yellow bloom, presenting the last, great feeding opportunity for many insects before the doors of winter slam shut. In an orgy of life amazing to witness, butterflies, beetles, bees, ants and wasps swarm these hearty desert plants, foraging, breeding and fighting to claim each blooming bracket as their own. During the warm days of autumn, a curious insect can be seen throughout the gap, darting across the dry ground at rapid pace, its curled antenna constantly moving as it searches for small flowers and insects. Its abdomen and

Rabbitbrush blooms in autumn. (John Clement photo)

thorax are covered with what looks like crushed red or yellow velvet. This is the velvet ant, really a solitary, flightless wasp capable of a severe, defensive sting, also known as the "cow killer."

In August, large numbers of hatch-year California gulls push west through the gap, leaving the Columbia Basin for the beaches of the eastern Pacific Ocean, where they feed and loaf the remaining warm days of the season away. These gulls will return through the gap by late November to escape the coastal storms dropping out of the Gulf of Alaska. Often the warm dog days of fall are clear and windless in the gap and very dry. By October the gray and green rabbitbrush has gone to seed, and very few plants are flowering. Insect populations have dropped off, and songbird migration is almost finished. More waterfowl now appear out on the delta and on the waters of the gap as these birds drift in from the north. These early transient ducks and geese mix with resident birds as they feed and fatten in preparation for the approaching winter. At 340 feet above sea level, the gap often remains relatively warm well into late October. However, winter often makes a few preemptive strikes by firing a few frigid days into the gap, killing off many insects and struggling plants. When these sudden cold snaps hit, the wind out of the gap can wail at better than 60 miles per hour. Even the omnipresent ravens take shelter during these sudden weather changes. Now the gap changes once again as it has done for eons from warm and dry to very cold and damp. The winter season's grip is firm and never ignored by animals and plants within this ancient site.

A Winter's Day

The first hint of the new day is only a lighter shade of gray in an opaque sky. A pair of common ravens drops out of the cold basalt rims to investigate the discovery made on the highway below by a raucous group of black-billed magpies. Yet another cottontail rabbit lies just to the side of the white line along the highway, crushed by indiscriminate tires, sightless eyes glazed open, front teeth protruding in a seeming half smile as the magpies jostle for position. These striking, long-tailed, black-and-white avian scavengers have already ripped into the still-warm rabbit. One raven lands on the highway and with deliberate steps moves to flush the magpies off their meal. A passing car in the next lane does the job, and the ravens take possession of the rabbit.

Sheets of broken ice layer the shoreline along the great river in the gap. A few herring gulls slowly paddle out off Port Kelley. These large four-year gulls (four years to reach maturity) come south out of coastal Alaska and Canada near the end of September and arrive in the lower Columbia Basin to spend the winter feeding at the base of the dams on dead and injured fish, around the giant feedlots just northeast of the mouth of the gap and at city landfills. Cold, gray clouds hang just above the basalt rims at the eastern end of the gap as flocks of dark-eyed juncos move through the bunchgrass and islands of remnant sage in search of grass and forb seeds. Amid much outer-tail feather flashing, mock chasing and constant chipping, these wonderful birds bring a spark of life to a cold, quiet slope. These native, black-hooded sparrows perform an altitudinal migration each fall as they move down out of the Blue Mountains into the lower Columbia Basin.

Reaching in between pockmarked rocks, probing every crack and depression, pressing its head and body deep into dark recesses, an adult canyon wren hunts for dormant insects and frozen spiders, as it eagerly works a steep talus slope along the northwest flank of the gap. Periodically, it returns to some cold surface rock to utter its superlative song of descending notes or a simple "*chee-tech*" type call to bring notice to any other wren within earshot that it is still alive and holding territory. This perky, native wren lives year-round in the basalt talus slopes of the gap.

A cold breeze blows to the west across patches of crusted snow as a small group of mule deer browses on clumps of grass and Russian thistle near the edge of a rocky wash about halfway up the face of the southeastern side of the gap. These native deer move slowly, their large ears cocked in different directions, listening for the slightest sound out of place. With moist noses working the dry, chilled air, they catch only the scent of a porcupine just beyond them. No threat registers and they resume feeding.

Porcupines are solitary cavity-dwelling rodents that live within the basalt rims of the gap. They will inhabit the same, deep

Horned grebe in winter. (Paul Clement photo)

cavity for years, venturing out to feed on western juniper, sage and willow during the night and returning to their warm dung-floored cavities by first light. Ever alert for coyotes and mountain lions, the porcupine always leaves itself an avenue of escape or defense.

By midmorning, small snowflakes tumble from the gray-white clouds down into the gap as the wind increases. Ice has formed out on the Walla Walla River Delta, sealing it off from most birds or mammals until the next thaw. Yet a tight flock of dunlin persistently searches for open areas where they can probe for invertebrates in the cold mud, determined to remain on the delta as long as there are opportunities to feed. Considered a coastal species by most, this gray and white, black-legged sandpiper has wintered on the delta annually since 1993 in low numbers.

Out off Sand Station at the southwestern end of the gap, large rafts of waterfowl form: mixed flocks of Canada geese, mallards, greater and lesser scaup, American wigeon and redheads as well as dense rafts of American coots. This section of the gap also attracts horned and western grebes, common loons and, rarely, Pacific loons that survive on rough fish species. The ducks and geese attempt to evade the 107-day-long waterfowl hunting season and tend to approach land at dusk to feed after most human waterfowl hunters have retreated for the day.

Dry, powdery snow dusts the tops of 10 or so long-abandoned cliff swallow nests firmly adhered to a slight overhang high up one of the many basalt cliff faces. The developers of these round, mud-daubed nests are far to the south – hawking insects out over tropical pastures. Their intact nests now perform double duty during the cold of winter in the gap. Chunky dark finches fly into several of the swallow nests, uttering mellow "*tu-tu*" notes as they press into the sphericity of the space to roost and pass the frigid night. These gray-crowned rosy-finches are a wintering species that arrive from high elevation breeding sites in the Cascades, Rockies, Alaska or Wallowa mountains. Unique in appearance and physiology, wrapped in pale grays, dark and light milk chocolate browns with flushes of pink dusky rose, these winter finches often form large, roving flocks that swirl and settle to feed intensely on seeds and sprouts where the wind has swept the snow away.

By midafternoon this day is at its warmest, all of 16 degrees Fahrenheit with a dusting of dry snow blown like fine sand around the plants and rock formations. A lone rough-legged hawk flaps and glides out over the icy gap in a fruitless attempt to locate a thermal. This buteo in subadult plumage is often mistaken for an adult bald eagle due to its white head and tail and black belly. Hunting on the ground, this circumpolar species arrives in late September filling the same niche as the Argentina-bound Swainson's hawk.

Only the common ravens make any noise in this cold, quiet landscape as they move past the ramparts of great basalt rims frosted with light snow in their daily reconnoiter of the gap. Late in the day the loud roar and rumble of several trains shatter the winter silence and leave behind their diesel fumes. Near Port Kelley and its grain terminals, far more than 200 ducks gather to dive and feed on submerged sprouting wheat spilled in the process of loading the grain onto barges for the trip downriver to distant ports. Redheads, canvasbacks, ring-necked ducks, greater scaup, and common and Barrow's goldeneyes, plus dozens of American coots all forage off this huge offering of food. They will stay near the grain terminal until nightfall and then move out into the great river and raft up.

On broad, dark wings a wintering adult bald eagle flies northeast toward its evening roost site in the Two Rivers Habitat Management Unit on McNary National Wildlife Refuge. This big scavenger-predator has spent the day catching and feeding on dead and wounded ducks and geese brought down by waterfowl hunters but never recovered. Several subadult bald eagles fly into the gap just behind the adult bird. They lack the white head and tail of the 5-year-old adult. With heavy crops they also move toward the winter communal evening roost along the Columbia River at the Two Rivers Habitat Management Unit, leaving the diving ducks at Port Kelley nervous and jumpy. An average of 30 eagles will gather to roost here for the night. The cold, pale gray sky darkens as this short winter's day fades over the gap, once again inviting the nocturnal denizens of this snow-sprinkled desert out to hunt. Spring is less than five weeks away.

Wallula Gap an Island Desert

This unique desert area has been subject to rapid catastrophic changes by weather, flood, wind and fire. Yet, these are changes that this natural system has had and can deal with over time. It is Western man that has brought the greatest alterations to this site and forever changed the future of this island desert. Surrounded by a sea of intensive agriculture and ever-expanding human populations, Wallula Gap will be hard-pressed to maintain both its native species and the genetic diversity of those resident native species as other nearby wild lands vanish and those populations are lost.

So much has already occurred in this wild island desert that has changed how we live and think here in the lower Columbia Basin. What will time and Wallula Gap bring us next?

Bibliography

Adamus, P.R., K. Larson, G. Gillson and C.R. Miller, 2001, *Oregon breeding bird atlas*: Oregon Field Ornithologists, P.O. Box 10373, Eugene, OR 97440. CD-ROM

Alderfer, J., ed., 2006, *Complete birds of North America*: Washington, D.C., National Geographic Society, 696 p.

Allen, Grover M., 1939, *Bats*: Cambridge, Massachusetts, Harvard University Press (Dover edition, 1962: New York, Dover Publications, Inc.), New York, 368 p.

Altman, Bob and Aaron Holmes, 2000, *Conservation strategy for landbirds in the Columbia Plateau of eastern Oregon and Washington*: Oregon & Washington Partners in Flight, 97 p.

Barbour, Roger W. and Wayne H. Davis, 1969, *Bats of America*: Lexington, Kentucky, The University Press of Kentucky, 286 p.

Bent, Arthur C., 1932, *Life histories of North American gallinaceous birds*: Washington, D.C., United States National Museum, Smithsonian Institution Bulletin 162, 490 p.

Box, Jayne Brim and Jeff Kershner et al, 2003, "Historical distribution and taxonomy of freshwater mollusks of the western United States": Freshwater Mussels of the Pacific Northwest Workshop, Abstracts, U.S. Fish and Wildlife Service, Columbia River Fisheries Program Office, Vancouver, Washington.

Burns, Jim, 2004, *North American owls: Journey through a shadowed world*: Minocqua, Wisconsin, Willow Creek Press, 216 p.

Cody, Robin, 1996, *Voyage of a summer sun: Canoeing the Columbia River*: Seattle, Sasquatch Books, 301 p.

Contreras, Alan, 1997, *Northwest birds in winter*: Corvallis, Oregon, Oregon State University Press, 264 p.

Corkran, Charlotte C. and Chris Thoms, 1996, *Amphibians of Oregon, Washington and British Columbia*: Renton, Washington, Lone Pine Publishing, 175 p.

Cullinan, Tim, 2001, *Important bird areas of Washington*: Olympia, Washington, Audubon Washington, 170 p.

Dauble, Dennis D., 2009, *Fishes of the Columbia Basin*: Sandpoint, Idaho, Keokee Books

Davis, James Luther, 1996, *Seasonal guide to the natural year: A month by month guide to natural events*: Golden, Colorado, Fulcrum Press, 399 p.

Denny, Mike, 2006, "The Russian olive and its utilization by wild birds in the Columbia Basin of Washington and Oregon": *WOS News 103*, Washington Ornithological Society, Seattle, 4 p.

Dobler, F.C., J. Eby, C. Perry, S. Richardson and M. Vander Haegen, 1996, "Status of Washington's shrub-steppe ecosystem: Extent, ownership, and wildlife/vegetation relationships": Research Report, Washington Department of Fish and Wildlife, 7 p.

Evanich Jr., Joseph E., 1990, *The birder's guide to Oregon*: Portland, Oregon, Portland Audubon Society, 288 p.

Evens, Howard Ensign, 1993, *Pioneer naturalists*: New York, Henry Holt & Company, 294 p.

Ferguson-Lees, James and David Christie, 2001, *Raptors of the world*: New York, Houghton Mifflin Co., 992 p.

Gabrielson, Ira N. and Stanley G. Jewett, 1940, *Birds of Oregon*: Corvallis, Oregon, Oregon State College (Dover edition, 1970, Birds of the Pacific Northwest: New York, Dover Publications, Inc.), 650 p.

Gilligan, Jeff, Mark Smith, Dennis Rogers and Alan Contreras, eds., 1993, *Birds of Oregon: Status and distribution*: McMinnville, Oregon, Cinclus Publications, 330 p.

Hoffmann, Ralph, 1927, *Birds of the Pacific states*: Cambridge, Massachusetts, The Riverside Press, 353 p.

Jewett, S.G., W.P. Taylor, W.T. Shaw and J.W. Aldrich, 1953, *Birds of Washington State*: Seattle, University of Washington Press, 767 p.

Knick, S.T. and J.T. Rotenberry, 1995, "Landscape characteristics of fragmented shrubsteppe habitats and breeding passerine birds": Conservation Biology, v. 9, no. 5, p. 1059-1071.

Knittle, K. and L. Knittle, 2005, *Birds in Washington State: A county comparison*: Washington Birder, 2604 NE 80th Street, Vancouver, WA 98665, 64 p.

Kozloff, Eugene, 1984, *Plants and animals of the Pacific Northwest*: Seattle, University of Washington Press, 264 p.

Lord, W.R., 1902, *A first book upon the birds of Oregon and Washington*: Portland, Oregon, J.K. Gill Company, 297 p.

MacMahon, James A., 1985, *Deserts* (The Audubon Society Nature Guides): New York, Chanticleer Press, Inc., 638 p.

Marshall, D.B., M.G. Hunter and A.L. Contreras, eds., 2003, *Birds of Oregon: A general reference*: Corvallis, Oregon, Oregon State University Press, 768 p.

Marshall, D.B., M. Chilcote and H. Weeks, 1992, *Sensitive vertebrates of Oregon*: Portland, Oregon, Oregon Department of Fish and Wildlife, 208 p.

Mattison, Chris, 1998, *Rattler: A natural history of rattlesnakes*: London, Blandford, United Kingdom, 141 p.

Nuttall, Thomas, 1903, *A popular handbook of the birds of the United States and Canada, New Revised and Annotated Edition* (by Montague Chamberlin): Boston, Little, Brown, and Co., 431 p.

O'Connor, Georganne and Karen Weida, 2001, *Northwest arid lands: An introduction to the Columbia Basin shrub-steppe*: Columbus, Ohio, Battelle Press, 218 p.

Opperman, Hal, 2003, *A birder's guide to Washington*: Colorado Springs, Colorado, American Birding Association, Inc., 635 p.

Paige, C. and S.A. Ritter, 1999, *Birds in a sagebrush sea: Managing sagebrush habitats for bird communities*: Boise, Idaho, Partners in Flight Western Working Group, 47 p.

Paulson, D., 1993, *Shorebirds of the Pacific Northwest*: Seattle, University of Washington Press, 406 p.

Phillips, H. Wayne, 2001, *Northern Rocky Mountain wildflowers*: Guilford, Connecticut, Globe Pequot Press, 284 p.

Pyle, Robert Michael, 2002, *The butterflies of Cascadia*: Seattle, Seattle Audubon Society, 420 p.

Richardson, Scott A., 1996, "Washington State recovery plan for the ferruginous hawk": Washington Department of Fish and Wildlife, 63 p.

Rising, James D., 1996, *A guide to the identification and natural history of the sparrows of the United States and Canada*: San Diego, Academic Press, Inc., 365 p.

Ross, Alexander, 1849, *Adventures of the first settlers on the Oregon & Columbia River*: London, Smith, Elder & Co., 379 p.

Sackschewsky, M.R. and J.L. Downs, 2001, "Vascular plants of the Hanford site": Richland, Washington, Pacific Northwest National Laboratory publication no. 13688, 64 p.

Sibley, David A., 2000, *The Sibley guide to birds*: New York, Alfred A. Knopf, 544 p.

Smith, Michael R. et al, 1997, "Breeding birds of Washington State: Volume 4 in Washington State Gap Analysis – Final Report" (K.M. Cassidy, C.E. Grue, M.R. Smith, and K.M. Dvornich, eds.): Seattle, Seattle Audubon Society Publications in Zoology,

No. 1, 538 p.

Storm, Robert M. and William P. Leonard, eds., 1995, *Reptiles of Washington and Oregon*: Seattle, Seattle Audubon Society, 176 p.

Strong, Emory, 1959, *Stone Age on the Columbia River*: Portland, Oregon, Binford and Mort, 254 p.

Swain, R.B., 1957, *The insect guide*: New York, Doubleday & Co., 261 p.

Taylor, Ronald J., 1992, *Sagebrush country: A wildflower sanctuary*: Missoula, Montana, Mountain Press, 211 p.

Townsend, John K., 1839, *Narrative of a journey across the Rocky Mountains to the Columbia River*: Philadelphia, H. Perkins & Co., 189 p.

Turner, Angela and Chris Rose, 1989, *Swallows and martins: An identification guide and handbook*: Boston, Houghton Mifflin Co., 258 p.

Wahl, T.R., B. Tweit and S.G. Mlodinow, eds., 2005, *Birds of Washington: Status and distribution*: Corvallis, Oregon, Oregon State University Press, 436 p.

Walter, Sunny and Janet O'Mara, 2001, *Washington nature weekends: Fifty-two adventures in nature*: Guilford, Connecticut, Globe Pequot Press, 271 p.

Watters, G.T., 1994, "North American freshwater mussels, Part 1: The quick and the dead": *American Conchologist*, v. 22, no. 2, p. 4-7.

Weber, John W. and Earl J. Larrison, 1977, *Birds of southeastern Washington*: Moscow, Idaho, University Press of Idaho, 66 p.

White, Mel, 1999, *Guide to birdwatching sites, western U.S.*: Washington, D.C., National Geographic, 240 p.

Ziswiler, Vinzenz, 1967, *Extinct and vanishing animals: A biology of extinction and survival*: New York, Springer-Verlag, 133 p.

American Indians from the Columbia Plateau used these stones as net weights in fishing. (Maxey Museum)

5

Pre-history:
The Walúulapam at Wallula Gap

Catherine E. Dickson

"To the Indian, there was only one place where he belonged – in his homeland made sacred by the ageless sleep of his ancestors, made fruitful by the spirit of his children yet unborn. Here and only here could the life rhythm of his race beat on in unbroken harmony. To tribes all over the land, the earth was their mother, wise and loving in her care for her children. Our love, therefore, is a kind of mystical devotion, for this wise mother has cradled our race since the beginning of time. She has been dedicated with the life-blood of our ancestors and made sacred with their graves."

–Maudie C. Antoine, Chairwoman, Board of Trustees, Confederated Tribes of the Umatilla Indian
Reservation on June 11, 1955, in Walla Walla at the 1855 Treaty Centennial

Pre-Contact History of the Columbia Plateau

Archaeologists divide the past into phases. For the Columbia Plateau, phases are generally defined by characteristic artifacts and occasionally by features like the housepit. From the artifacts and features they find on the surface and during excavation, archaeologists hypothesize about the activities people were engaged in and then try to understand why things changed over time. The relationship of the artifacts to each other and to the features is critical to developing the hypotheses; that is part of the reason why looting is so destructive. It is illegal in both Oregon and Washington to excavate archaeological sites without a permit.

Many phase chronologies have been developed for the Columbia Plateau, but they aren't entirely consistent with one another. As a general rule, there has been a gradual shift from a nomadic existence exploiting a broad spectrum of resources to semi-sedentism centered on major rivers but still utilizing many other resources. Archaeologists hypothesize that changes in the way people lived in the past relate to changes in the environment (especially climate), people's relationships with their neighbors (i.e., the introduction of new ideas), and adaptations to the place in which people live over time.

Very little archaeological work was undertaken in the Wallula area prior to the construction of McNary Dam. By that time the site referred to as Wallula was already badly looted. Some earlier large-scale archaeological excavations had been undertaken along the Columbia River downstream of Wallula; others were undertaken along the lower Snake River. Therefore, an understanding of the human past at Wallula is based on what people in the surrounding

area were doing. This information is further influenced by an understanding of the culture of the people who lived in this area when Euro-Americans first invaded it. It is important to remember that the Walúulapam (Walla Walla Tribe) believe their ancestors have been in the Wallula area since time immemorial.

The human history of Wallula is tied to its geology. Near the end of the Pleistocene Epoch, beginning about 15,300 years ago and ending about 12,700 years ago, a series of major floods down the Snake and Columbia rivers washed away any evidence of human presence and activity. The earliest period for which there is archaeological evidence on the Columbia Plateau is called Clovis, based on a type of fluted spear point first found in Clovis, New Mexico. This period is estimated to date from between 11,500 and 11,000 years ago. On the plateau, only one site with subsurface materials has been documented by archaeologists; therefore, the lifestyles of the people living at this time are poorly understood. It appears that they had a well-developed social/religious system that involved sophisticated ceremonies. The people apparently hunted large animals, perhaps including mammoths, with spears. The relationship between the people who used Clovis spear points on the plateau and those who followed is not clear.

The people who lived in the Wallula area between about 11,000 and 8,000 years ago lived in small, mobile groups. Population density was low. Temporary shelters, including windbreaks and huts, were constructed as necessary. People foraged, gathering a wide variety of plant and animal resources, including fish (salmon, suckers, minnows), river mussels, deer, elk, antelope, birds, rabbits and hares. Small grinding stones, including thin cobbles whose edges have been ground flat, suggest the use of plant resources. Analyses have not determined precisely what people were grinding. People lived in small, tepee-like surface dwellings. Hunting technology switched from the spear to the atlatl (spear thrower, basically a wooden device that enables a person to throw a dart much farther). At this time, dart points were lance-shaped and stemmed. Flaked tools most commonly were made from chert. Fishing technology included nets, as indicated by net weights (a small cobble with two or more flakes removed to provide a point to which to tie the nets) and harpoons, which were both composite and single-piece. Hides were probably prepared with end- and side-scrapers. Bone needles suggest the sewing together of leather items and/or basketry. Antler wedges may indicate woodworking. Some individuals were cremated with offerings.

Between approximately 8,000 and 5,300 years ago, people continued to live a mobile, foraging lifestyle but broadened their subsistence base. They hunted deer, elk, sheep, rabbits, beaver, waterfowl, muskrats, marmots, salmon, other fish and turtles. They gathered river mussels. Grinding technology changed from the small, hand milling stone and edge-ground cobble to a hopper mortar consisting of: a base of relatively flat rock, a bottomless basket and a cylindrical pestle. This technology suggests people were processing tough roots. Tools during this period are generally simple and expedient; the composite harpoons and bone needles are not found. Dart points shift from the willow-leaf-shaped form to a large, side-notched point similar to those seen in the Great Basin. Atlatl weights were also found.

From about 5,300 to 4,000 years ago, people became more sedentary. Small villages of one to three semisubterranean housepits appear. There is evidence of the seasonal reoccupation of villages, a trait that will continue. Logically, there appears to be an increased emphasis on the exploitation of local resources, especially riverine resources; archaeologists find the most diverse assemblage of faunal remains during this period. Overall, there is an increase in the use of roots and salmon, there are fewer projectile points, and the flaked stone tools are of poor quality. Hopper mortars continue to dominate the ground stone tools. Dart points are both side- and corner-notched. There is little archaeological evidence of this period in the Wallula area.

Beginning about 4,000 years ago, people began to store food to get them through the winter. Storage pits and processing ovens are now found within villages. Sites dating to this period indicate that people had base camps and collecting locations to exploit one particular resource, for example fish, game, roots, or mussels. Bone tools are well-made and include large needles, leisters (spears armed with three or more barbed prongs for catching fish), beads and gaming pieces.

About 2,500 years ago, there is evidence that people began to utilize the uplands more intensively, especially for harvesting roots. For the first time, archaeologists find antler handles for digging sticks. Earth ovens indicate camas was cooked, probably a preparatory step for storage. Both hopper mortar bases and deer, elk, sheep and bison bones are found in upland sites. Dogs may also have been part of the diet. Villages increase in size, consisting of 100 houses in some places. Salmon remains a critical element of the food supply. There is some evidence of intergroup strife and social inequality. The bow and arrow is adopted during this period, although atlatls continued to be used for quite some time. The materials from which flaked stone tools were made increase in quality and diversity, possibly indicating increased trade. Artifacts and artistic styles show a strong coastal influence.

The settlement and subsistence patterns of this period resemble those of the ethnographic period. Populations increased and people used new areas of the plateau. Longhouses, a new house form that is basically a semisubterranean housepit split in half and elongated, are seen after 1,500 years ago. Net weights, a common artifact, changed in size and style over time, perhaps indicating changes in or new varieties of nets. Other typical artifacts include harpoons and barbed bone arrowheads, other fishing implements, cordage, matting, basketry, needles, bows and arrows. Arrowheads become smaller and are often corner- or basal-notched. Fishing,

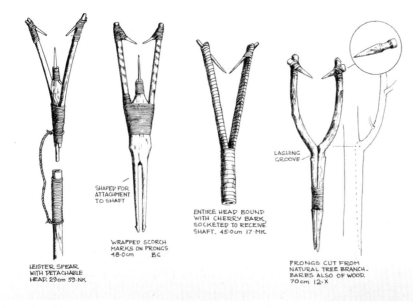

Examples of leister spears. (Hilary Stewart, 1982, with permission)

storage of salmon and storage of camas were all important.

Around the year 1720, the horse reached the Wallula area, changing some aspects of the culture. Mobility increased; most notably, expeditions were mounted to the Great Plains to hunt bison. Some elements of the material culture of Plains tribes were adopted by plateau cultures. However, the underlying culture continued to rely on a seasonal round centered on salmon fishing, root gathering, and deer and elk hunting.

Introduced European diseases decimated the Walúulapam's and other plateau tribes' population. The people persisted through that and other efforts at ethnic cleansing. On June 9, 1855, the Walúulapam, together with the Weyíiletpuu (Cayuse) and the Imatalamláma (Umatilla) signed a treaty and became the Confederated Tribes of the Umatilla Indian Reservation. These people continue to exercise their traditions and protect places, like Wallula Gap, that have always been important to them.

Archaeology near Wallula Gap

Pre-inundation excavations at pre-contact villages focused on sites downstream from Wallula Gap. These excavations took place in the 1950s primarily under the leadership of Joel Shiner and Douglas Osborne as part of the Smithsonian Institution's River Basin Survey project. Shiner's work followed Osborne's; Shiner incorporated Osborne's findings in his understanding of the Plateau culture area. Shiner's work was good for the time, but it was before radiocarbon dating and before volcanic ash layers could be tied to specific eruptions. Therefore, his and Osborne's attempts to understand change over time are based exclusively on relative dating techniques, usually involving projectile (spear, dart, arrow) point styles. Complete analysis of the artifacts Shiner and Osborne recovered has never been published. These assemblages have the potential to answer many more questions about the Plateau's past.

Shiner found cultural material at several sites beneath a layer more than 1 foot thick of volcanic ash now known to be from the eruption of Mount Mazama about 7,700 years ago that created Crater Lake. At one site, he found burned bones of rabbits, deer, salmon and other fish; flakes made up of 53 percent basalt, 31 percent chert (cryptocrystalline silica), 10 percent quartzite and 6 percent obsidian; fire-cracked rock; hammerstones; choppers; leaf-shaped projectile points; flakes used for cutting or scraping; and decorated bone beads. Features included hearths and mussel shell lenses (discrete deposit of shell that shows up within the stratigraphy). No evidence of shelter was found, but the number of artifacts suggested occupation over quite some period of time. Shiner hypothesized that shelters consisted of brush or mat and were not supported by large posts.

Another site was occupied soon after the Mazama ash fell. Here, Shiner found a bowl-shaped housepit. He suspected that the superstructure was light, perhaps mat-covered poles with soil banked against the lower edges. Matting fragments were observed on house floors. Artifacts at this site included specialized fishing equipment such as the net weight (notched, grooved and perforated). Not surprisingly, there was also an increase in numbers of fish bones, including salmon, sucker and trout. Choppers were more carefully made. Bone beads, bone awls, a bone projectile point (side-notched) and an antler tine pressure flaker were recovered. Projectile points at first were of the same style as before, but obsidian was used as a

material. Scrapers and knives were the same, but there were more long basalt knives. It appears that hopper mortar bases were observed but not recognized as such.

Later occupations involved saucer-shaped housepits that apparently had superstructures similar to their bowl-shaped predecessors. The houses became slightly smaller over time. The pits were used repeatedly; Shiner found floors superimposed upon one another. They were recognizable by a thin, dark charcoal stain. Large concentrations of fire-cracked rock were observed, once within an old housepit, and interpreted as earth ovens. Projectile points changed in size and shape over time. Choppers became more specialized, and the basalt knives were no longer used.

The late prehistoric period is well-reflected in the one site Shiner excavated that was not a winter village – the Wallula site. Near the mouth of the Walla Walla River, on a gravel bar was what appeared to be a fishing site. "In some places the soil was black, almost greasy, with charcoal, and salmon vertebrae were present in vast numbers," wrote Shiner in 1961. Shiner concluded that fishing was the main activity at the site, but the number of deer and elk bones and projectile points also hint at hunting. Pestles and bowls suggested to Shiner that seeds and berries might have been ground.

Arrowheads were numerous, small, stemmed or barbed, and made of petrified wood, basalt, agate, jasper, obsidian and bone. Net weights had two or four notches or were grooved. Hammerstones and choppers (or a combination of the two) were common. Mortar bases, anvils, pestles and stone bowl fragments were observed. Woodworking tools included stone and antler wedges, ground stone mauls, and flaked stone drills. One schist pipe bowl fragment was recovered. Bone awls and needles were of various shapes, usually made out of deer bones. An antler gaming piece, smooth on one side and decorated with small drilled pits on the other, suggests a leisure time activity. The presence of seashells here and at other sites indicates trade with coastal people. No evidence of any kind of shelter could be found, and this site, unlike the villages Shiner and Osborne excavated, was subject to seasonal flooding.

Life at Wallula Gap

Reading archaeology reports, it is often easier to visualize artifacts than to see the people who were using them. Below is a brief scene of life in the Wallula Gap area, approximately 2,000 years ago.

•••

The boy awoke, earlier than usual, to an explosion. His sister giggled as he jerked upright at this familiar yet always surprising noise a rock makes as it blasts apart. While he slept, his mother, grandmother and sister have stirred the fire in the center of the dwelling, fetched fresh water, and heated river-rounded stones found along the beach. With wooden tongs his mother grabbed another red-hot stone from the fire, rinsed the ash off, and dropped it into the tightly woven basket with the morning's stew. This rock, however, apparently lacking cracks or other imperfections, held together, transmitting its heat to the breakfast.

The boy yawned and stretched. The fire warmed his feet. His bearskin blanket was becoming too warm. But the tule mat lying over a mattress of last year's grass and the shredded inner bark of the cottonwood tree fit his shape perfectly. And though he was hungry, he could not muster much excitement about breakfast: dried fish stew with the tiniest amount of camas flour to thicken it up, exactly

Edna Kash-Kash, a Cayuse woman, outside a rush-mat covered tepee, circa 1900 (Taylor and Sturtevant, 1991, p. 109). (National Anthropological Archives, Smithsonian Institution, negative 76-15867)

the same thing they had eaten for two weeks, since they finished their fresh venison.

Dinner, however, would be different. Today, the women would go up on the bluff to the spot where the sun shone on the rocky soil throughout the winter, and where the celery first poked up through the rocky ground. While hunting rabbits, he had noticed the tiniest green shoots a week earlier and raced back to the village with the news. His grandmother rolled her eyes at his desire for her to go gather up the plants immediately. No one in the village had eaten fresh vegetables since last fall, but as he well knew, there was a time to gather, and until that time came, everyone would wait.

The elders had decided it was time to start getting ready for the Celery Feast. The boy smiled. He jumped up and reached for his cedar root basket from which to eat his breakfast stew. He caught his mother's eye and turned to straighten his bed.

The tepee-like, conical, semisubterranean dwelling in which he, his sister, his parents and grandparents spent the winter was about 15 feet in diameter. The village consisted of several dwellings aligned parallel to the shoreline above the floodplain. Nearer to the shore were small, round, mud-covered sweat houses. Storage buildings and pits were interspersed amongst the dwellings. Many years ago, the grandparents had found a free spot in the village and had begun to build their house. Using two Indian hemp ropes, they formed a cross, driving stakes at each end of each rope. They then placed additional stakes, forming a circle. Using their kápin (digging sticks), the women of the village began to excavate the circle to a depth of approximately 12 inches. They put the sand in baskets and piled it around the outside of the circle.

Having completed the hole, three lodgepole pine poles

Kápin (digging sticks). (Department of Anthropology, Smithsonian Institution, negative 95-20810)

(which had washed down the Walla Walla River) were lashed together with stinging nettle twine. These poles were approximately 18 feet long. They were raised, the bases braced against the sides of the newly dug housepit, and spread to create a tripod. Additional poles of willow were then placed with their butt ends in the hole and tips leaning against the tripod frame until there were about 12 poles.

On top of this wooden frame the grandparents placed tule mats. The tules had been collected in late summer, after the summer steelhead run, from the mouth of Juniper Canyon. The goal was to gather strong, straight plants of approximately the same diameter. The women brought them back to the village to dry. The grandmother used two willow twigs, each approximately 4 feet long, as guides to trim the tules to the same length. A long, thin, greasewood needle or punch pierced the tules, a few at a time. She bound the tules together with dog bane twine she had rolled on her leg. Binding the skinny ends of the tules together, she created a mat to fit the conical shape of the structure. (When a straight mat was desired, the grandmother alternated skinny and fat ends.)

When the mats were 10 to 20 feet long, the grandfather tied them to the wooden poles, beginning at the bottom. About four tiers of mats were required to reach the top of the house. He piled four mats on top of each other on the bottom tier, three on the next tier up, then two, and only one at the top, carefully overlapping each tier approximately two inches to encourage the rain to run off. The grandparents leaned additional willow poles against the outside of the house to secure the mats in the strong winds, leaving a large gap at the top to allow the smoke to escape and to let the light in.

The door, facing east toward the river, was an arch left open in the tules. Another tule mat (this one straight rather than conical) was placed with the tules parallel to the ground. In nice weather, this door could be rolled up and secured.

The grandmother piled bark, grass and the soil removed from the inside of the house around the outside of its base. In very cold weather, she hung elk skins on the inside walls. She placed her fire roughly in the center, with her family members' beds encircling it. Some personal items were hung from the poles; others were stored at the heads of the beds. When the family left the village to gather berries and hunt, they removed the superstructure, storing the posts until they returned, taking the tule mats with them. When they returned to the village, laden with winter stores, the grandmother and her daughter swept out the accumulated sand and reassembled the house.

This place, Wallula, made a good winter village for a variety of reasons. A little way up the Walla Walla River, tribal members could gather river mussels at the rapids and find an ideal place for a weir; they could catch sturgeon in the deep water of Nč̓í wana (the Columbia River), gather driftwood commonly deposited in accessible eddies, and most likely find a spot near the confluence that did not freeze solid. Of course, it never occurred to the boy that he would winter anywhere else – his family had always been here. His people were known as the Walúulapam, the people of Wallula.

After breakfast, the women of the village gathered with their Indian hemp flat bags (decorated with lighter colored grasses) in which to place the celery shoots and set off to the south. They were pleased with what they saw. The winter had been cold and wet. The plants coming back up were plentiful and strong. The girl, having watched her mother, grandmother, aunts and cousins gather foods since she was in her cradleboard, needed no training for this task.

Her grandmother was proud that she filled her bag as quickly as some of the older girls.

Within a few hours, everyone's bag was full, and they returned to the village to prepare for the feast. It was a fine day, so the women sat in the arbor to peel the shoots. The arbor, with its flat tule mat roof and three brushy sides, served as both a sun and wind block. Each woman and girl had several sharp chert flakes with which to peel any skin too thick to chew. Having slept poorly the night before on account of excitement about her first celery gathering, the girl had clumsy fingers. A sharp flake dug deeply into her palm. She quickly went to the edge of the village and gathered some yarrow leaves with which to staunch the flow of blood. She crushed them between two rocks, secured the leaves with a piece of leather, and returned to the arbor to continue work.

Unbeknownst to the boy or his sister, the men had placed bundles of cedar splints along the shoreline for use as torches and had spent much of the night in their canoes, successfully using the jacklights to catch whitefish and suckers. The fish would be added to the celery shoots making a great feast with which to say a thankful farewell to winter and turn their minds to spring.

When all the food was ready, the people gathered to eat. Since the wind had died down, they were able to lay tule mats outside. The women sat on the south side, the men on the north side. The singers gathered at the west end with their drums and sang songs of thanks, winter, and spring. Then the young women brought out basket after basket of whitefish, suckers, roots and all of those things individual families had saved through the long winter for this day – dried gooseberries, service berries, raspberries, huckleberries, currants, chokecherries and even a little bit of dried deer.

When all the food was arrayed on the mats between the men and women, and everyone could hardly stand to wait any longer, one more prayer was said, one more song was sung, everyone drank a bit of chúush (water) and the feasting began.

Talk turned to the spring and summer to come. Soon the men would go up the Walla Walla River a short distance to rebuild the weir. Years ago, their ancestors had placed willow posts at intervals across the river. Every few years they rebuilt the curtains of small willow branches to attach to the posts. These curtains would be lowered, blocking the fish, which could then be collected in a 15- to 18-foot-long net – with wooden floats and notched cobble weights – pulled by two people, or by a single person with a dip net.

The dip net, used most commonly when water roiled and visibility was poor, required an ability to feel the fish. One of the boy's uncles was particularly skilled. His dip net had a long vine maple handle and a hemp net. The tip of the handle was bent around to form a hoop from which to hang the net. The uncle stood on a platform at the edge of the rapids and swung his net in the water, downstream with the current. When he felt a fish, he pulled up the net, deposited the fish on shore, and returned the net to the river, almost in a single movement. The boy often worked with him, clubbing the fish with a polished, cylindrical rock. He caught approximately 100 fish per day.

Stories abounded of fishing for spring chinook from canoes. The boy listened carefully, trying to learn all the tricks his uncles would play on him in an effort to make him lose his balance and take an unplanned swim. He would continue to practice with his harpoon – last year he had broken many wooden practice points as he missed the salmon and hit the rocks below them. The adults' harpoon tips were made of deer antler, the foreshaft of part of a deer ulna. Attached to the main cedar shaft with Indian hemp twine, the foreshaft when released absorbed the initial impact of the fish moving away from the spear, prevented the main shaft from breaking, and allowed the large salmon to tire before being hauled ashore.

Since the spring chinook run would begin soon, the women talked of reconstructing the salmon drying/smoking sheds and racks that had been dismantled for winter. They discussed who

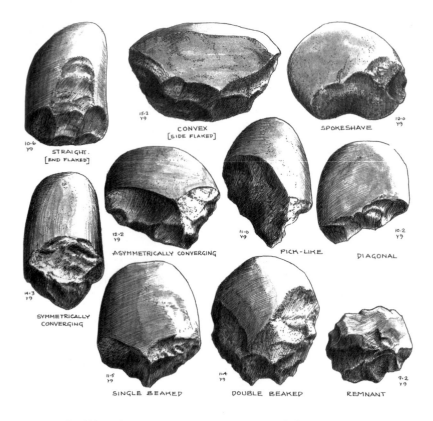

Examples of pebble tools. (Hilary Stewart, 1996, with permission)

would be staying at Wallula for the summer and who would go to the mountains, following spring as it moved up in elevation. The grandmother's thoughts turned to root feast, which would be coming along in a couple of months.

She recalled the work she had done to prepare her granddaughter for her first root digging. She had worked on a kápin since last summer when she gathered huckleberries in the mountains. She had gone to the same area from which her grandmother had gathered the wood for her kápin. Singing a song of thanks, along the way she had stopped at a creek to inspect the cobbles. She grabbed one, assessing the fit in her hand and the material. She frowned at a hairline fracture in the rock, threw it back, and continued her singing walk along the creek. Ah, there it is, she thought as she stooped down and picked up an oval, gray, river-rounded basalt cobble larger than her hand. She turned a circle, looking for another rock that could be used as a hammerstone, and saw a fist-sized quartzite cobble. She sat down on the ground in the shade. With four blows, she had made a hand axe. Two flakes had been removed from one side of the larger cobble and two from the other, creating a sharp, pointed surface. The other end of the cobble retained its smooth, river-rounded surface and fit comfortably in her hand.

Upon reaching a grove of ocean spray, she eyed it critically. She was looking for a limb about the diameter of a deer's lower leg that would reach from her feet to her chest, with just the right curve, something akin to the bend of the steelhead's back as it jumped along the rapids below Wallula. She talked softly to the ocean spray, giving thanks and seeking assistance; she received the help she sought. She could see the finished kápin. She opened one of the pouches she wore around her neck and removed a sharp flake. She cut off several small branches so she could reach her limb. Four swings of the hand axe and it was hers. With her strong hands she removed the leaves, branches, and some of the bark. She returned to camp.

The previous fall after the salmon run, back at Wallula, she directed her husband not to come home without a bull elk with kápin handle antlers. He and a small group headed into the mountains along a well-worn trail. They began by traveling up the Walla Walla River, then turned south and traveled overland toward the Umatilla River, which they reached the second day. Next, they walked up 'Iskúulpa Creek. They passed deer and cow elk. On the third morning they built sweat, believing they could find an elk that day. That afternoon, he watched a young bull trying to control his harem, the man chuckling at the little guy who thought he was so big. He knew this bull would never satisfy the grandmother, and more importantly, would not provide his granddaughter with a kápin handle to last her into adulthood. He heard his nephew's meadowlark whistle and shook his head. It was so wrong, it never ceased to surprise him that every animal in the forest did not run from the sound. He answered with a perfect raven call and moved toward the rest of the party.

At the edge of a meadow he saw them: two big, branch-antler bulls grazing within 200 yards of each other. They were not yet in the rut, not yet worried about harems. It was a nice day, and the grass was greening up from the recent rain. He saw his nephew and sons. All knew it would be his shot. He breathed deeply and said a silent prayer to the elk as he assessed the animals. He chose the smaller of the two, out of respect for the larger, and removed his bow from his shoulder. He had made this bow from juniper and backed it with elk

sinew. He had painted it green (using ocher) with red (from another kind of ocher) and yellow stripes (using the inner bark of Oregon grape). He reached to his right side where his otter pelt quiver rode by his waist. He chose the syringa shaft with the obsidian point he had obtained along with a variety of other items for a sheephorn bow on his last trip to Celilo Falls. He recognized the arrow by its goose feather fletching. In the blink of an eye the elk turned to look toward him, took a dozen steps, and fell. The grandfather and his companions approached the animal and thanked it for its sacrifice.

The youngest of the party cut the animal open with a sharp chert knife with an antler haft. He field dressed the elk. The others helped to skin, butcher and package the meat and other parts of the animal in grass mats and baskets. The men, confident of their success, had brought little food. Having completed preliminary preparations, they shared the liver, heart and kidneys. They smoked and slept. The next day, they placed the baskets on their backs and began the trip back toward Wallula. On the way home, they killed two deer and processed them in the same way as the elk. Over the course of a year, approximately 20 to 30 deer or six to 10 elk would be needed to feed one family.

For 15 minutes the grandmother noted every flaw in the antler the grandfather presented, but he could see in her eyes that she was pleased. Back at the village at Wallula, she spent a few hours sawing through the antler with one sharp basalt flake after another, coupled with sand to act as an added abrasive, to remove the femur-length tine to use as the kápin handle. She gave the remainder of the antler to her daughter to make into pressure flakers, wedges and knife handles. Having removed the tine, she began the process of drilling the hole for the actual kápin. On nice days she sat outside, out of the wind, with her basalt drill. Around her were people repairing dip nets, sharpening knives, pecking and grinding a stone bowl, or making shell, stone, and bone beads. She looked at the Two Sisters and told the story of how they came to be there. As she told the story, she closed her eyes and could see her grandmother telling the same story in the same spot in the same way, also with her eyes closed. She knew her grandmother had been seeing her grandmother, and that her relatives had been telling this story in this spot since the day those girls turned to stone. Everyone quietly listened to the story as if it were the first time they had heard it.

Having completed a hole of the appropriate size, she returned to the stick. She had long since used some of her chert flakes to remove all the bark and cambium layer, removing about one-half inch all the way around. She had used a piece of scoria to sand the wood into a smooth surface. She had reduced the overall length to approximately her granddaughter's waist. One end came to a dull point. This end she had put in a fire whose coals were past red-hot and used the heat of the fire to strengthen the wood. Now was the time to fit the stick and handle together. She fit the handle over the stick, but had to remove a little more of the wood from the digging stick. Perfect now. She grabbed a cobble and tapped the antler, wedging it into place on the digging stick. She heated some spruce pitch on a flat rock near the fire and used a stick to spread it all around the handle/stick junction.

At the Celery Feast, the women's conversation turned with eager anticipation to late summer, when the myriad trails that passed through Wallula would bring old friends, family and interesting strangers to the village. There would be races, gambling, singing, dancing, trading and romance.

After dinner, once the young women had cleaned up and distributed the leftovers (with the best going to the elders), it was time for more singing and dancing. The girl, exhausted by her long day, was soon curled up on a corner of the tule, sleeping. Her brother intended to dance all night, but replete with the rich foods he had been dreaming of for months, he could not keep his eyes open. The grandmother covered them with an elk skin and returned to her husband to celebrate another year in which the land surrounding Wallula had met the needs of its people.

Bibliography

Ames, Kenneth, 2000, "Review of the archaeological data," *in* "Cultural affiliation report," edited by the National Park Service, Washington, D.C.

Dickson, C.E. and C.D. Carley, 2002, "Miimá Taymút: A historic properties management plan for the John Day Reservoir, volume II: Ethnography, history, and archaeology" (Submitted to the U.S. Army Corps of Engineers, Walla Walla District, under contract number DACW57-99-M-0617): Mission, Oregon: Confederated Tribes of the Umatilla Indian Reservation, Cultural Resources Protection Program.

Karson, Jennifer, ed., 2006, *Wiyáxayxt/Wiyáakaaawn = As days go by: Our history, our land, and our people – the Cayuse, Umatilla, and Walla Walla*: Pendleton, Oregon, Tamástslikt Cultural Institute, 265 p.

Ray, V.F., 1939, "Cultural relations in the plateau of northwestern America": Los Angeles, The Southwest Museum, 154 p.

Rice, H.S., 1985, "Native American dwellings and attendant structures of the plateau": Cheney, Washington, Archaeological and Historical Services, Eastern Washington University Reports in Archaeology and History 100-44.

Shiner, J.L., 1961, "McNary Reservoir: A study in plateau archaeology" (River Basin Surveys Paper No. 23): Washington, Smithsonian Institution, Bureau of American Ethnology.

Stewart, Hilary, 1982, *Indian fishing: Early methods on the northwest coast*: Seattle, University of Washington Press, 181 p.

Stewart, Hilary, 1996, *Stone, bone, antler, and shell: Artifacts of the northwest coast*: Seattle, University of Washington Press, 140 p.

Taylor, C.F. and W.C. Sturtevant, 1991, *The Native Americans: The indigenous people of North America*: London, Salamander Books, 256 p.

Walker, D.E., ed., 1998, "Plateau," *in* W.C. Sturtevant, general editor, *Handbook of North American Indians*: Washington, D.C., Smithsonian Institution, v. 12, 791 p.

In 1841, Joseph Drayton, a member of the Charles Wilkes Expedition, drew this work titled "Fur Trappers, Walla Walla." It shows Archibald McKinley, Fort Walla Walla's chief trader, standing at its river gate inspecting pelts exhibited by Indian women. Three months after Drayton's visit the fort burned. (Oregon Historical Society, 56364)

6

History in the 19th Century: Wallula's Three Economies

G. Thomas Edwards

"The country around about has sometimes been represented as fruitful and beautiful. I am obliged to deny so foul an imputation upon the fair fame of dame Nature. Desert describes it as well as it does the wastes of Arabia."

–Thomas J. Farnham, *An 1839 Wagon Train Journal*

During the 19th century Wallula played a major regional role in three different economies – fur trading, gold mining and railroading. Fort Nez Perce (sometimes spelled Fort Nez Percés and later called and better known as Fort Walla Walla) established above the mouth of the Walla Walla River that emptied into the Columbia River served two fur companies from 1818 to 1855. Because of its regional importance, historians have written far more about British Fort Nez Perce's role than the American town's subsequent history, a period that also shaped life on the Great Columbia Plain. In 1860 American speculators created Wallula, a small, rag-tag appearing river port on the site of the abandoned fort. For about eight years this depot was a bustling entrance to distant mining camps. In the early 1880s, a new Wallula, about a mile east of the first one, became a significant railroad center, serving two major lines and some local ones, and falling to competing towns by 1890.

The Fur Trade Era

From 1814 to 1821, the North West Company (NWC) of Montreal dominated the fur trade in the distant Pacific Northwest. The company's most accomplished explorer, David Thompson, who had made several journeys into the rugged terrain of the upper Columbia River system, descended the river in 1811. Near the Snake River's mouth, "He met with Walula [*sic*] Indians who asked him, as they had asked Lewis and Clark, to establish a trading post."[1] These Indians desired a local post trading guns, cloth, beads, metal goods, tobacco and other items. At the time they met the explorer, tribesmen on this section of the Columbia could obtain these objects only through a trade network originating at the river's mouth. These

experienced native traders assumed that a nearby post would offer more goods at better exchange rates. Thompson understood their request and said it would be met.

Seven years after Thompson's assurance, the NWC honored his promise by constructing Fort Nez Perce at a site above Wallula Gap. This was one of five posts built on the Columbia or its tributaries; each was expected to gather furs and send them to Fort George, at the river's entrance. They would then be shipped to China. Fort Nez Perce played a critical role in a plan designed to establish a fur monopoly in the vast Snake River region. According

1853 engraving of an American Indian encampment along the Columbia River just north of Old Fort Walla Walla. This second Fort Walla Walla is adobe; the earlier wooden fort had burned. To the south is Wallula Gap, with the Twin Sisters in left-center. (Isaac I. Stevens, 1860, "Reports of explorations and surveys, to ascertain the most practicable and economical route for a railroad from the Mississippi River to the Pacific Ocean": United States War Department, v. XII, book I, plate XLII.) (Whitman College and Northwest Archives)

to historian Richard Mackie, it was "a frontier to be turned into a fur desert to discourage American overland interest in the Columbia."[2]

In July 1818, David McKenzie of the NWC and diverse workers, including Canadians, Iroquois and " Owhyhees" (Hawaiians), arrived to build the log post mostly from driftwood about a half mile north of the Walla Walla River.[3] After lengthy and tense negotiations with several tribes – fully detailed by fur trader Alexander Ross – workers constructed the isolated fort and profitable operations began. Although the post was built on the homeland of the Cayuse and Walla Walla tribes, McKenzie called it Fort Nez Perce. Ross, who had knowledge of NWC posts in the trans-Rocky region, considered Fort Nez Perce to be "the most hostile spot on the whole line of communication."[4] Many visitors, including Hudson's Bay Company (HBC) leader Governor George Simpson, disliked the post's environment: "A more dismal situation than that of this post can hardly be imagined. The fort is surrounded by sandy desert, which produced nothing but wormwood."[5]

Writing about 140 years later, geographer D.W. Meinig agreed with Simpson: "It would have been difficult to find a more bleak and unattractive site: a barren gravel terrace overlooking the Columbia, but a view blocked on the south and west by basaltic walls, and to the east extending over the drab sagebrush plain to the lower Walla Walla Valley." The scholar insisted, however, that dreary Fort Nez Perce was "the key strategic position west of the Rockies."[6]

The fort's design was as unique as its arid location. It had two walls, and Indians were allowed only past the outer 20-foot wall with its positions for cannons and muskets. A 12-foot inner wall protected houses and a storehouse. Ross stated that water was stored "as a security against fire, the element we most dreaded in the designs of the natives."[7] With walls built to prevent scaling, numerous firing positions, and the sage slashed to keep natives from getting to the post undiscovered, the fortification was called by some the "Gibraltar of the Columbia."[8] An American visitor in 1832, however, counted only six defenders and concluded it was "merely sufficient to frighten Indians."[9]

In September 1818, McKenzie left the new fort heading for the Blue Mountains with 55 men and nearly 200 horses to trap in the Snake's tributaries. For many years brigades dispatched by the NWC or later by the HBC trapped and explored an enormous region. In the 1820s Alexander Ross, Peter Skene Ogden, John Work or others led expeditions to trap beavers in remote places. "The Snake Country hunts originated," a historian explained, "in what is now Washington State and operated in present-day Oregon, Idaho and Wyoming. Parties connected with the hunt traveled over parts of present-day Arizona, Nevada and California."[10] In 1824 the HBC – it had acquired rival NWC in 1821 – vigorously continued the harvesting of furs in the Snake River country.

Assembled at Fort Nez Perce, the brigade included both employees of the company and freemen, independent trappers receiving pay for each pelt. The HBC preferred that both groups be sent on the Snake brigades rather than to remain at company posts, where they could become embroiled with nearby Indians. Ross stated that the company collected "the refuse about the different establishments" for the expedition. This included "all the lazy, cross-grained and objectionable among the engaged class; the superannuated, infirm and backsliding freemen, the wayward half-breed, the ignorant native; and last of all, the worst of all, the plotting and faithless Iroquois."[11]

American Joseph Drayton, a member of Lieutenant Charles Wilkes' naval expedition, observed that Canadians and Iroquois Indians complained to strangers, but not to their HBC employers, about low wages and scanty food. "No American," he judged, "would submit to such food, including coarse, unbolted bread, dried salmon, fat (tallow), and dried peas."[12]

While much has been written on HBC male employees, historian Jennifer Ott has recently summarized and emphasized the role of brigade females, unofficial members who dressed furs and performed other useful tasks.[13]

Many travelers utilized the fine HBC bateaux designed for Columbia River traffic, watercraft described by Drayton during a journey to Fort Nez Perce. These strong vessels were 30 feet long, had a 5.5-foot beam and carried 3 tons. Each had eight oarsman and a steersman, who demonstrated great skill in navigating rapids. The bateaux were easily carried around portages along with the standard 90-pound bales, consisting of groceries, clothing, munitions and trade items.[14]

In late fall the brigades departed Fort Nez Perce, trapped during the winter and returned in late spring. The fur brigades required scores of horses because many died on the rugged routes or became food for the hungry expedition. Besides short rations the trappers endured other hardships, including freezing weather and icy streams; their work was, Ogden sympathized, "a most laborious one and one that in four years makes a young man look almost as if he had reached the advanced age of 60."[15]

Upon the brigade's return to Fort Nez Perce in the late spring, workers loaded the precious pelts upon several bateaux bound for Fort Vancouver – it had replaced Fort George – where workers would store them aboard a vessel sailing to England or China. A few weeks after the last craft went downriver to Fort Vancouver, boats loaded with trade goods, supplies and passengers returned to Fort Nez Perce and other interior forts.

Assisted by a staff averaging five or six, the post trader – the resourceful Duncan McGillivary served for a time in this responsible position – prepared the brigades. Servicing them was the post trader's most important responsibility, but he also had several other important assignments. Utilizing an interpreter, he conducted a profitable local trade with regional Indians who brought beaver pelts, hides (wolves, muskrats, river otters), horses and food, including salmon, sturgeon, dogs, horses, roots and rabbits. Trading mostly in the fall, these shrewd nearby natives bargained for tobacco, files, kettles, knives, cloth, guns, powder, beads, blankets and other items.

Because beaver pelts meant HBC profitability, the post trader encouraged local Indians either to trap animals or to trade for them with distant tribes. He closely evaluated the furs harvested by the Cayuse and other tribes, and, of course, this trade led to bitter haggling over values. One of the post trader's most important assignments was to negotiate with the Nez Perce and Cayuse for horses and then protect them from loss or theft.

The post trader at Fort Nez Perce did not face the physical and personnel difficulties of Snake brigades, but he handled challenging assignments, including evaluation of the work ethic of employees, maintenance of the fort's security and supervision of gardens. Governor Simpson investigated the post in 1824 and complained about its expenditures, including the costs of imported food and other local expenses. He charged that during a three-year period those at Fort Nez Perce had consumed 700 horses and costly imported food. To meet Simpson's demand for efficiency, the post trader oversaw the raising of swine and cattle and the growing of corn, pumpkins, potatoes and radishes along the nearby Walla Walla River.

The actions of the so called "fort Indians" – Walla Walla, Cayuse, Nez Perce and others – angered HBC leaders. In 1828, Governor Simpson expressed a low opinion of them: "the Natives who are a bold Warlike race do little else than rove about in search of Scalps, plunder and amusement."[16] He insisted, however, that the fort's personnel must stay on friendly terms with these troublesome Indians. In 1832 Nathaniel Wyeth, an American visitor, had a more positive view, concluding that corn was raised three miles from the fort and "none was stolen by the Indians, a good test of their honesty as they are all most [sic] always starving."[17] John Kirk Townsend, an American ornithologist, visited the post in 1834 and described the fort Indians as "a miserable, squalid looking people" who lolled around the post and annoyed visitors "by the importunate manner in which they endeavor to force them into petty trade for a pipe, a hare

or a grouse." The scholar learned that industrious tribesmen engaged in distant trade and that local Indians, suffering from privations, would not steal from an unguarded tent and thereby demonstrated more honesty than citizens residing in "Christian communities."[18]

Dr. John McLoughlin served the HBC as chief factor of the Columbia River Department. He ruled Indian tribes firmly and justly. In 1834 he concluded that the Fort Walla Walla was "one of the most troublesome posts (if not the most troublesome) in the Country."[19] The severest challenge occurred in 1836 when Cayuse and Nez Perce tribesmen tied up chief trader Pierre C. Pambrun, releasing him only after he agreed to increase payments for furs and horses. Pambrun and other HBC leaders would warn missionaries and travelers about these mercurial Indians.

But the fort Indians often proved useful, providing food,

Old Fort Walla Walla: In December 1871, *Scribner's Monthly* carried an essay entitled, "Pictures from the Plains." This unusual illustration shows the remnants of Fort Walla Walla, a few business buildings and hunters carrying bales of buffalo robes. The accompanying story states the fort was "also on the general route from the mines to San Francisco."

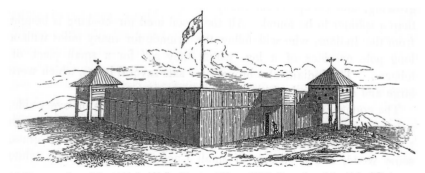

1841 engraving of Fort Walla Walla (Charles Wilkes, 1845, Narrative of the United States Exploring Expedition During the Years 1838, 1839, 1840, 1841, 1842: London, Wiley and Putnam, v. IV, p. 391.)

For a few years in the 1880s, Wallula was a critical rail junction, serving the OR&N coming from the west across the bridge over the Walla Walla River, the NP coming from the north, and a line from Walla Walla and other points coming from the east. The NP and ORN both constructed facilities and their employees contributed to the local economy. In 1889 the NP moved its facilities to Pasco, and the OR&N moved its structures to Umatilla. As a consequence Wallula declined. (Jeff Asay, 1991, Union Pacific Northwest: The Oregon-Washington Railroad & Navigation Company: Edmonds, Washington, Pacific Fast Mail, p. 37) (Oregon Historical Society negative 74146)

furs, horses and labor. In 1841 the wooden post burned, and Indians made adobes used in its immediate reconstruction. Trusted tribesmen carried messages to other posts, and occasionally they engaged in horse races with HBC workers, whose Indian wives lived within the fort and sometimes exercised considerable control of their mates.

Driftwood gathered from the Columbia's banks warmed the fort's residents during long, cold winters. These inhabitants, however, probably complained more about the intense summer heat than the winter's cold. French Canadians had far more experience with harsh winters than furnace-like summers. "The climate is hot," an American visitor complained, "and every thing about the fort seemed so dry, that it appeared as if a single spark would ignite the whole and reduce it to ashes."[20] HBC personnel, unaccustomed to living in

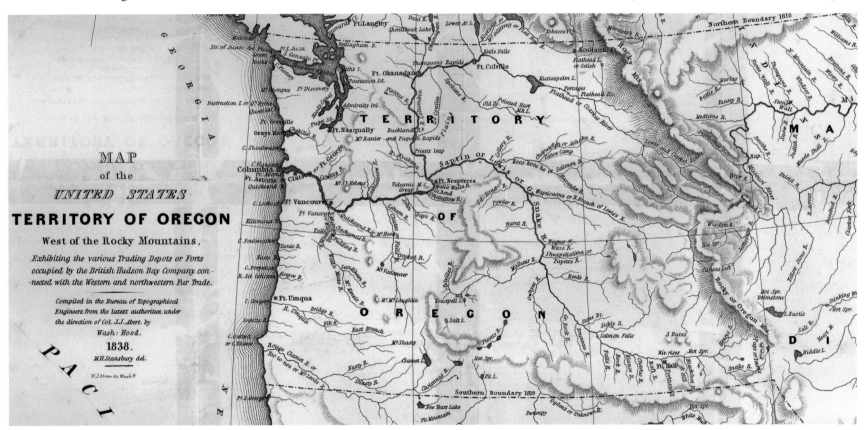

Drawn in 1838, this map has been modified to show an incorrect international boundary line of 1846, and the Territory of Oregon established in 1848. The Hudson's Bay Company's forts are shown, but missionary stations are excluded. (Whitman College and Northwest Archives)

a treeless land, often commented about this unusual environment, contrasting it with that below The Dalles, a region of trees and wooden dwellings. Fur traders, similar to American farmers arriving in the 1840s, judged that lands east of the Cascades were inferior to those west of the range.

During Governor Simpson's tour of the Columbia Department in 1824-25, he had observed this sharp contrast in landscapes but did not relocate Fort Nez Perce downriver. Instead he ordered that it be moved across the Columbia because a future Oregon boundary line would most likely give the south and east banks to the United States. Enjoying a rewarding trade, nearby tribes strenuously objected to a relocation. McLoughlin, who sought to avoid a confrontation with these protesters, ordered that the fort should remain in place.

Many HBC leaders came by watercraft from Fort Vancouver to Fort Nez Perce – a journey of nine days – and in the 1830s Americans crossed the Rockies by horseback, sought the post's assistance, and described its conditions. In 1832 New England merchant Nathaniel Wyeth – who had ambitious plans to break the HBC's economic monopoly – enjoyed many courtesies extended by Pambrun at Fort Nez Perce. He received a warm welcome and expressed surprise about conditions: "At the post we saw bull and cow & calf, hen & cock, punkins [sic], potatoes, corn, all of which looked strange and unnatural and like a dream."[21] He wrote that the HBC employees ate considerable horse meat and traded for numerous skins. The fort's two major purposes were, he concluded, trade for horses and protection of the communication line. Ornithologist John Kirk Townsend, who came westward with Wyeth two years later, traveled with a nine-boat brigade from Fort

Vancouver to Fort Nez Perce, and took an excursion along the Walla Walla River, killing five of the numerous rattlesnakes and bagging 22 grouse.

In 1834 Benjamin L.E. Bonneville, an army captain on leave, made a brief visit. Apparently he had told the Nez Perce that American traders would arrive and undersell Fort Nez Perce.[22] More importantly, Dr. Marcus and Narcissa Whitman and other Presbyterian missionaries, serving the American Board of Commissioners for Foreign Missions (ABCFM), arrived in 1836 after a fatiguing cross-country trip. Eliza Spalding and Narcissa were the first women to cross the continent. Pambrun expressed profound pleasure in meeting them. According to historian Frances Fuller Victor, "The kindest attentions were lavished upon them from the first moment of their arrival, when the ladies were lifted from their horses, to the time of their departure; the apartments belonging to the fort being assigned to them, and all that the place afforded of comfortable living placed at their disposal."[23] The missionaries, like other westbound travelers, had eagerly anticipated the fort's amenities, including appetizing meals and comfortable beds. Narcissa, the first American woman to describe Fort Walla Walla (the name now used), expressed great pleasure in having a room sheltering her from the sun. Its portholes for firearms and a loaded cannon behind the door created no concern. The missionary proclaimed that the fort's animals were "the largest and fattest cattle and swine I ever saw."[24] But she complained that high winds whistling through Wallula Gap shook the fort and made conversation difficult.

After locating their mission at Waiilatpu about 25 miles distant from the fort, the Whitmans received food, a stove, animals and other essentials from Fort Walla Walla. Dependent on the HBC, Dr. Whitman sometimes practiced medicine or spoke on religion at this regional oasis. Closer in distance to post traders than their fellow missionaries, the Whitmans considered these HBC employees and their Indian wives to be their neighbors, a sentiment that was reciprocated. Post trader Archibald McKinley, for example, warned a Cayuse that an insult to the Whitmans was one to himself and that HBC would punish Indians who might harm missionaries.

In 1838 Reverend Jason Lee passed through the fort on his way to the East, where he sought to convince his Methodist leaders to send reinforcements and money to strengthen his Willamette Valley colony and to open new missionary stations. He also had a political agenda: He wanted the joint occupation of Oregon terminated in favor of the United States. Sharing Lee's expansionist sentiments, Whitman and Henry Spalding also requested that the ABCFM send a very large missionary reinforcement. In late 1838 two Catholic priests arrived in Oregon and enriched the religious life of French-Canadians, including those at Fort Walla Walla. There was a major change at the post when McKinley, a Scottish Presbyterian, replaced Pambrun, a Catholic. During the 1840s the post's personnel heard the religious conflict between priests and preachers as each sought Indian converts. Perhaps some white traders or travelers might have been reminded of the bitter colonial controversy over souls and lands that had triggered wars between French Catholics and English Protestants and of the heated current controversy in the United States between Protestants and Catholics. Few natives around Fort Walla Walla committed to Christianity, but a few chose one of the competing churches.

In 1847 Whitman and other missionaries, participating in these religious quarrels, expressed new fears of Catholic influence when Reverend A.M.A. Blanchet came to the post as bishop of the Walla Walla Diocese.[25] But well into the 1840s, HBC fur traders and missionaries in the Walla Walla Valley respected and befriended each other; furthermore, the HBC consistently aided Protestant missionaries and American farm families, most of whom were Protestants and eager to live under the American flag.

Thomas Farnham was one of the first Americans receiving Fort Walla Walla's generosity. Arriving in October 1839, he, too, found Pambrun to be hospitable and to share his admiration for Napoleon. But the visitor criticized the environment: "The country around about has sometimes been represented as fruitful and beautiful. I am obliged to deny so foul an imputation upon the fair fame of dame Nature." Farnham concluded, "Desert describes it as well as it does the wastes of Arabia."[26]

American military travelers also rested and purchased necessities at Fort Walla Walla, a well-known post. In 1842 the HBC's naval brigade rowed a contingent from Lieutenant Charles Wilkes' naval squadron up the Columbia. Wilkes communicated what Joseph Drayton reported: "On approaching [Fort] Wallawalla the scenery becomes grand: the country is broken into volcanic peaks, forming many fantastic shapes, resembling figures and colossal heads: many of them are seen either insulated or in groups; some of them are known under the name of Nine-pins. Through this pass of volcanic rocks the wind rushes with great violence in summer, to supply the rarefied portion above. The current had increased very considerably: it often became necessary for the voyageurs to take a pipe, or in other words, a rest."[27] When the brigade came into view, an employee hoisted the company's flag over the sand-and-dust-covered fort.

Arriving at Fort Walla Walla about a year later, explorer John C. Frémont described it as sited on "bare sands, from which the air is literally filled with clouds of dust and sand." The lieutenant concluded that he saw "the great river on which the course of events for (the) last half century has been directing attention, and conferring historical fame."[28] Frémont purchased eight horses, dried salmon and potatoes and hired "an intelligent Indian boy ... to accompany us as far as The Dalles." Passing through Wallula Gap, the explorer complained about loose sand and volcanic rock. Heeding the warning made at Fort Walla Walla, he took precautions against thieving Indians living on the Deschutes River. Frémont assumed that "emigrants to Oregon" would end their overland travel at Fort Walla Walla, construct boats and paddle downriver. Afraid of the dangerous river, only a minority would choose this route. The vast majority preferred to drive their teams south of the river to The Dalles.

In the 1840s, religious controversy did not threaten HBC's power in the region. But there were two significant challenges: the decline in the fur trade and the arrival of American families traveling the Oregon Trail. In 1844 the drop in the number of pelts brought to the post was, according to historian Mackie, "a reflection of the company's scorched earth frontier policy and trade disruptions caused by American overlanders using the company's Snake Brigade route" through forts Hall, Boise and Walla Walla, making it part of the Oregon Trail.[29] In 1843 Jesse Applegate, a noted traveler of this route, and some of his companions at Fort Walla Walla exchanged their cattle for HBC cattle to be received at Fort Vancouver. Some men constructed six mackinaws from driftwood, employed an Indian pilot, loaded 60 men, women and children on the vessels, and descended the Columbia. Applegate watched a young son drown when a boat overturned. This tragedy was by no means unusual; a number of HBC personnel had drowned in the turbulent waters between Wallula Gap and the Cascades. Ogden told Drayton that he had witnessed the drowning of 10 employees in a single accident at The Dalles.[30]

In 1846, the United States and Great Britain signed the Oregon Treaty establishing the boundary at the 49th parallel, an agreement placing Fort Walla Walla in American territory. The British firm had anticipated its loss, and in 1848 its brigade traveled a northern route, bypassing the fort's "danger zone."[31]

The post played a role in the spread of regional disease. Recent scholarship has shown that measles was first reported at Fort Walla Walla in June 1847; in November it struck the Cayuse at Waiilatpu and led to an attack on the Whitman Mission on November 29, 1847.[32] Indians murdered the Whitmans and 12 others and held 47 terrified captives, including 37 children. HBC employees, who would not leave the post until 1855, played a major role in assisting the survivors of the Whitman massacre. Soon after the brutal attack by a band of Cayuse, William McBean, who was then in charge of Fort Walla Walla, relayed the tragic news to Fort Vancouver and prepared his post – it had only four men and two priests as defenders – against a possible Cayuse assault. HBC leader Peter Skene Ogden hurried up the river, reinforced the fort and ransomed the captives held at Waiilatpu.

The Whitman massacre triggered the Cayuse Indian War, initiating, historian Alvin Josephy explained, the "violent phase of the white man's conquest of the newest corner of the Republic."[33]

In this, as well as subsequent wars, volunteers or regular soldiers came through Wallula Gap and camped around Fort Walla Walla. During the Yakima War, Indian agent Nathan Olney, fearing the Walla Walla tribe, in late 1855 convinced the HBC leader at the fort to dump ammunition into the Columbia and to abandon the post. Soon after, Walla Walla Indians pillaged and burned portions of it. HBC employees soon returned – as the 1846 Oregon Treaty had allowed – and resumed the sale of goods, especially to the retired French Canadians, living in a nearby colony called Frenchtown. These farmers now resided in Washington Territory, a political entity created in 1853. Superintendents of Indian affairs Isaac I. Stevens (Washington) and Joel Palmer (Oregon) utilized the post for meetings associated with the significant Walla Walla Council of 1855.

Beginning in the early 1850s, Fort Walla Walla was important to homeseekers following a new route. In 1853 Congress appropriated $20,000 to build a military road linking Fort Steilacoom with Fort Walla Walla. Hoping to attract Oregon Trail travelers, Puget Sound boosters, not soldiers, built in 1853 a rough wagon road through the forested Naches Pass and along the Yakima Valley to a connection with the Oregon Trail at Fort Walla Walla. In that year 29 wagons ferried the Columbia River on a flat boat made of driftwood, but in the 1850s few wagon trains chose this hazardous route.

In 1856 the American Army reestablished Fort Walla Walla about six miles from the destroyed Whitman's mission and supplied it from a dock and a warehouse built near the site of abandoned Fort Walla Walla. Thus began a close relationship between the former British trading post site with interior American military forts.

When HBC employees abandoned the damaged fort in 1855, the bleak structure indicated the end of a meaningful period of regional history. But this inactivity soon ended. The mining frontier of the 1860s, especially into what became Idaho and Montana, would bring renewed activity as a bustling river port emerged upon the old Fort Nez Perce site. The mining rush passed through Wallula Gap, establishing Wallula as a significant river port in Washington Territory.

The Mining Era of the 1860s

In 1860 speculator James Vansyckle founded Wallula as a depot to serve an anticipated gold rush into eastern Washington Territory and to serve travelers who would travel on the Mullan Road, a 600-mile route linking Fort Benton on the Missouri with Wallula.[34] Completed by the army in 1862, it promised to be an improved route to the Pacific Northwest. Vansyckle and other speculators anticipated making sizable profits from thousands of prospectors and overlanders. Wallulans could sell necessities to weary immigrants in much the same way as traders at The Dalles supplied needy Oregon Trail travelers. In summary, it seemed that Wallula would prosper as a well-located depot. Although the Mullan Road did not attract numerous wagons of home seekers – it was more rugged than the Oregon Trail – the anticipated mining rush using the Mullan Trail and several routes into the eastern mountains met the expectations of speculators.[35]

Vansyckle's experience in Stockton in the 1850s shaped his early thinking about Wallula. Stockton, an instant California city, had enriched its early inhabitants because it linked San Francisco with Sierra Nevada mines. Wallula could have a similar experience: It would connect Portland with mountain mines. Vansyckle, who had worked for Wells Fargo in Stockton and Sacramento, also understood that gold seekers needed hotel rooms, stables, food, alcohol, hay, mining equipment, entertainment and transportation.

Hence, Vansyckle moved his family into the abandoned fort, tore down its fragile adobe front walls and platted Wallula

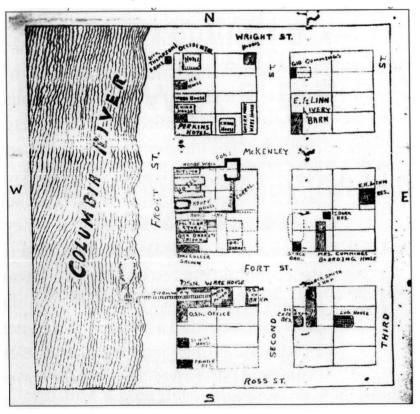

In 1862 promoter James Vansyckle sold lots as plotted on this Wallula map. (Whitman College and Northwest Archives)

with a partner. Despite a lack of a title, they offered 40 blocks of lots at prices ranging from $100 to $1,500. The promoters assured prospective buyers that the port, supplied by foodstuffs and grains from the productive Touchet and Walla Walla valleys, would successfully compete with landlocked Walla Walla as the supply center for overlanders and miners. Furthermore, in 1862 Wallula's proponents argued that prospectors would travel a shortcut to Lewiston bypassing Walla Walla. A few merchants believed the boosters and purchased lots fronting the Columbia. Teamsters hauled lumber from Walla Walla to the emerging river port, and it soon "lost the appearance of a desert sand bank and assumed

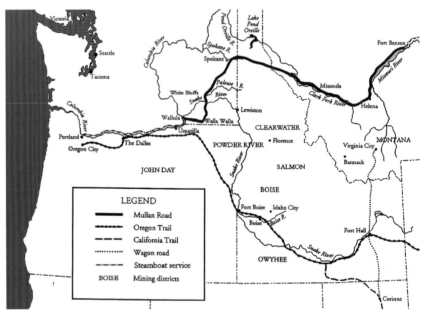

In the 1860s Wallula was a port linking the Columbia River with mining districts of Idaho and Montana. (G. Thomas Edwards, 2005, "Town Boosterism on Oregon's Mining Frontier: James Vansyckle and Wallula, Columbia Riverport, 1860-1870": Oregon Historical Quarterly, v. 106, no. 1, p. 79)

the more useful and becoming position of the head of practicable navigation."[36] Wallula looked like other regional river ports with its line of hastily constructed wooden business buildings sited about 100 feet from the water's edge.

In 1860 prospectors had discovered gold on the Nez Perce Reservation. In the next few years, miners enjoyed success at the Clearwater, Florence and Boise Basin districts; their rush resulted in the creation of Idaho Territory in 1863. Significant strikes, including the Bannack, were made in what became Montana in 1864. Prospectors also found gold, in lesser quantities, in northeastern Washington and northeastern Oregon. Thus, thousands of men

In the 1860s miners arriving by steamboat in Wallula could purchase supplies and arrange for transportation to Walla Walla or distant mining districts. Many travelers praised James Vansyckle for building a well-located port in a sandy, treeless environment. (Oregon Historical Society negative, CN016015)

and tons of supplies came by Oregon Steam Navigation Company (OSN) steamboats to Wallula or rival river ports. In 1862 eight steamboats a week churned from Celilo to Wallula.

Knowing, combining and adding the occupations that made money from those in a mining rush, Vansyckle profited from his store, hotel, saloon, hay yard and stables. In short, he and his competitors entered every profitable business. Although Wallula provided basic goods and services, it failed to attain regional dominance like Stockton. The boasted shortcut from the port to Lewiston attracted few travelers because teamsters reported heavier sands on this route than on the old Oregon Trail to Walla Walla. Travelers preferred a well-worn Nez Perce trail to Lewiston or the Mullan Road to Montana. Walla Wallans ridiculed Wallula's pretensions and easily overcame its challenge because of their advantages, including a much larger and richer hinterland and several able entrepreneurs, especially Dr. Dorsey Baker. Although Wallula failed to grow much beyond 100 permanent residents, it naturally became Walla Walla's vital port, and the economic interests of the two towns intertwined.

Like the HBC's Fort Walla Walla, Wallula also experienced an economic rhythm. Steamboats generally operated from March through December, the period of Wallula's greatest activity. Its businessmen endured a sluggish winter and were dependent upon renting quarters to miners, including Chinese, who waited for improved mountain weather. When the Columbia was cleared of ice, Wallula jumped to life, heartily welcoming OSN steamboats loaded with miners, animals and merchandise. This 240-mile-river-and-portage route originated in Portland, passed through The Dalles and generally terminated at Wallula. Workers carried boxes, bags, crates and sacks from the steamboats and piled them on Wallula's crowded beach. At a distance, horses, mules, oxen and cattle grazed on bunchgrass.

Vansyckle summarized the interior transportation system: "Trains come into the town, camp around the warehouse, turn their animals out and let them run until their cargo is ready. The same with ox teamsters; good feed from a half mile to any distance around Wallula."[37] Pack trains made up of 25 to 100 horses, six mule teams, and six yoke ox teams carried loads of nails, dry goods, boots, shoes, weapons, clothing, food, whiskey, tools and other commodities that brought good prices in Walla Walla or mining camps. Teamsters and mule skinners generally stopped in Walla Walla and so did operators

Wallula depended upon Columbia River steamboats bringing eager miners and numerous supplies from Portland. The OSN's *Tenino* avoided large boulders as it steamed from the Deschutes River to Wallula. (Oregon Historical Society negative, OrHi 9029)

of saddle trains whose occasional lack of horses slowed the movement of men and material. Two competing stagecoach lines ran between Wallula and Walla Walla and beyond to distant locations. An observer hailed "the knight of the whip" who could drive the dusty, rutted, 32-mile road in about six hours.[38] Express riders also carried mail, dispatches and gold between communities and camps.

In the 1860s Walla Walla was the commercial center, supplying prospectors with housing, animals, food and supplies. It also attracted thousands of miners who fled cold mountain camps, wintered in the city, and enjoyed gambling and drinking in notorious dives.

Groups participating in Washington's gold rush were characteristic of those that had been in California. Wallula's residents and visitors, like those in other Western mining societies, came from many nations. The gold seekers who passed through the port in 1862 were described by a correspondent of the *Oregonian* on August 7, 1862. "The people are of all casts and complexion, and nationality. The busy little Dutchman, the enterprising Yankee, the deliberative Missourian, the lymphatic China man, the sable African, and the indolent Indian." The writer failed to include two important groups: Mexican mule skinners and professional men, ranging from merchants to bartenders. "Preachers, lawyers, doctors and indeed all professions," an observer wrote, "and nearly all races are represented in the mines, but of all classes I believe the lawyers do the least work."[39]

Consequently, Wallula, like Fort Walla Walla, attracted a diverse population. The post had brought Indians from many tribes, half-breeds, French-Canadians, Scotsmen, Englishmen and an occasional Hawaiian. The HBC traders voiced elitism in responding to this diverse population: "The formal relationships among the men … exemplified both the class structure of the 19th-century England and a quasi-military ordering of relationships."[40] However, newspaper correspondents detailing the mining frontier more often made racist, not elitist, comments. While several writers sympathized with the noble Nez Perce of Idaho suffering from the invasion of miners, more correspondents made negative comments about Indians and Chinese. Few Blacks lived in Wallula, and one who opened a business was quickly run out of town. A historian recently concluded, "Nativism and racism … converged in California's gold fields, as white Argonauts competed with people of color and foreigners of all nationalities for riches from the Mother lode."[41] In summary, attitudes in Washington Territory's mines in the 1860s were those of California in the 1850s.

River ports on the San Joaquin and Sacramento rivers had competed for the mining trade in the 1850s; the same rivalry occurred on the Columbia-Snake system in the 1860s. Wallula struggled for domination as a depot against newcomers, especially Lewiston and Umatilla. Promoters of each river port argued that it offered the best route to the mining camps and towns. While Wallula lacked the population of these Idaho and Oregon competitors, it enjoyed advantages, especially a location near Walla Walla, the leading commercial and agricultural center. A sharp-eyed traveler, C. Aubrey Angelo, in 1865 judged that Wallula was "the main terminus of steam navigation to those bound for Idaho. Good stages with steady drivers await your arrival and convey you over a good road to Walla Walla."[42] Angelo believed that Wallula had a superior location in comparison to Umatilla and pointed out the heavy traffic leading from the river – pack trains headed for

Montana and wagons went to Idaho. The traffic was impressive; a historian stated in 1865 that "100 pack trains averaging 50 animals per train with each loaded with about 300 pounds carried 750 tons of freight from the Columbia River to Montana."[43] A San Francisco visitor observed that the city profited from trade with remote Wallula. Its merchants, seeking to get goods into Montana before the cold season, competed to find space on ships bound for Portland. "So great has been the rush to get goods aboard the Oregon steamers for Montana and Idaho territories that drays have been compelled to take their stand at the piers at 12 o'clock at night – everyone being zealous to get in ahead."[44]

In 1866 and 1867 Vansyckle, using the pen name "Cumtux," wrote a series of public letters portraying Wallula's weather, trade and population. He and others described the extremely cold weather during the winters of 1861-62 and 1865-66. In the first severe winter, Wallulans, similar to other Walla Walla Valley residents, struggled to feed and shelter their animals. In early 1866 the severe cold weather iced the Columbia, Walla Walla and Snake rivers. Ice banks 6 feet thick lined the Columbia. Families sleighed and skated, travelers walked their horses and mules across the Walla Walla, and men ventured out onto the Columbia, cutting ice to obtain water for their animals. In the summer, residents and visitors struggled with soaring temperatures; once it reached 112 degrees. During this summer heat, Cumtux reported that neither "man nor beast could work during the middle of the day without danger to life."[45] Transportation costs, as with weather extremes, received considerable attention. Similar to the Hudson's Bay Company, the OSN monopolized river traffic, enjoying great profits. Numerous travelers, shippers and residents often denounced steamboat rates, but they did not voice similar complaints about the charges imposed by mule skinners, teamsters, express riders, or others providing interior transportation. These operators necessarily competed.

By the late 1860s, the diminishing mining rush through Wallula disappointed steamboatmen, merchants, packers, miners and others. Discouraged miners abandoned unproductive camps, and many, especially regional farmers, returned home. There was another difficulty for Wallulans: The competition with distant cities, including St. Louis utilizing the Missouri River, won the struggle to supply Montana's mining camps and emerging towns. This sharp competition slashed Portland's shipments up the Columbia, and Wallula, of course, lost business.

Cumtux, who incorrectly believed that OSN's monopoly explained the decline in river traffic, moved to Walla Walla by 1870 and died a few years later. But prior to quitting his Wallula businesses, he joined other country residents in expressing pleasure that Walla Walla Valley agriculture was replacing mining as an economic base. Farmers and merchants profited from the sale of wheat, flour, oats, barley and vegetables that came through Wallula. Cumtux reported in 1867, "The road from Walla Walla to Wallula is literally lined with heavy freight teams, eight or ten yoke of cattle and four, six, eight and ten mule teams, all heavily loaded with flour are coming in every day."[46] Some wheat and flour sacks, like beaver pelts once shipped by HBC, went to England. The OSN had profited from upriver traffic to Wallula; now it made money shipping downriver from Wallula. Walla Walla Valley farmers, businessmen and shippers also profited from this wheat trade, but Wallulans had fared much better when thousands of miners and tons of supplies passed through the port. The most activity in the port occurred when

dozens of teamsters pulled into town with wagons burgeoning with wheat and flour. Wallula suffered from an economic decline and many families departed.

The Railroad Era

Wallula arose as a railroad terminus on a limited scale in the 1870s and on a major scale in the 1880s. In the early1860s Wallulans had joined Walla Wallans in promoting the construction of a railroad that would transport wheat, flour and other commodities from the agricultural center to the river port. Walla Wallan Dorsey Baker, a banker and merchant who was trained as a physician, had the courage, skill and resources to build the road eastward from Wallula. Overcoming many challenges, Baker built the Walla Walla and Columbia River Railroad Company (WWCR), a narrow-gauge line that finally reached completion in 1875. Many were amused by Baker's crude line between Wallula and Walla Walla, but historian Carlos Schwantes has found that his economies of construction using rough wooden ties and wooden rails topped with a thin strip of iron to act as a surface for the car wheels was typical of railroad lines built in Eastern states during the 1830s and 1840s. Baker prospered, especially from transporting wheat and flour to Wallula where residents made little money handling railroad freight. Workers lugged wheat sacks and flour barrels from railroad cars to warehouses and later carried these goods to steamboats.

Travelers, as well as farmers, also needed Wallula's services, including historian Frances Fuller Victor. In 1872 she praised "the bluffs bordering the Columbia" at Wallula Gap and the attractive Walla Walla River. But she complained: "The sand of Wallula is something to be dreaded. You find it scattered over the plate on which you are to dine; piled up in little hillocks in the corner of your wash-stand; dredged over the pillows on which you thoughtlessly sink your weary head; [and] setting your teeth on edge with grit, everywhere."[47] Many observers noted Wallula's decline, including a Walla Wallan who described it in 1880 as "a crumbling ruin. The only signs of life visible were a force of men loading railroad iron and another party engaged in tearing down the Rescue Hotel."[48] Travelers emphasized that Ainsworth, the Northern Pacific's construction town near the Snake River's mouth, was the most active location above Portland.

Although many visitors grumbled about their stays in Wallula or noted its decline, shippers emphasized that the depot handled an ever-increasing amount of wheat and flour that filled warehouses. Baker's railroad enjoyed a monopoly in hauling these commodities because draft animals could not compete with locomotives. His control of land transportation was similar to that of OSN's domination of river travel. Shippers and travelers often denounced the two monopolies operating in and from Wallula, the river's leading grain port.

This transportation system of rail and river was unable to carry the ever-increasing amount of wheat and flour being produced in eastern Washington. Furthermore, it was expensive to hire laborers to carry sacks and barrels from boats to rail portages around Columbia River obstructions.

In the early 1880s Henry Villard, a resourceful, German-born entrepreneur, would end this inefficient transportation system by constructing a direct rail linking the Walla Walla Valley with Portland. Earlier Villard had dominated the Willamette Valley's

transportation, and he sought the same advantage in the Columbia Valley. The financier also wanted the Northern Pacific Railroad (NP), which was building from Minnesota to the Pacific Coast, to utilize the Columbia's left bank and terminate in Portland, not on Puget Sound. To realize his ambitions, Villard in 1879 formed, with local and distant capital, the Oregon Railroad and Navigation Company (OR&N) and purchased the OSN which had previously acquired Baker's railroad. Hence, a more powerful monopoly emerged, controlling transportation between Portland and its expansive hinterland.

In late 1880 OR&N purchased about 35 acres of land east of Wallula from the U.S. government and would lay track down the river from this site, not from the old river location. For several reasons, the OR&N moved inland from the river port: It could avoid buying land at higher prices from Wallulans; it no longer needed a steamboat landing; it was easier to bridge the Walla Walla River upstream; and it needed more space for railroad operations than the old town provided.

To improve travel from Wallula to Portland, Villard employed Chinese and white workers to lay narrow-gauge track from Wallula to Celilo. Two years later in 1882, workers replaced this line with standard-gauge track and did the same with Baker's old route from Wallula to Walla Walla.

In the same year, the OR&N line reached East Portland. Trains left there at 5 p.m., stopped for breakfast at Wallula, and arrived at Dayton, Washington, at 11:45 a.m. Villard grumbled about the slow schedule and extensive night travel. A subordinate responded "that the condition of the track did not warrant much greater speed, and travelers would not be so likely to notice and complain of the speed in the dark as they would if the trains were run in daylight."[49]

This second location of Wallula was more than a meal stop on the OR&N. It became a pawn during the complicated chess match between Villard and Frederick Billings, president of the NP. According to Billings's biographer, he located and graded a line on railroad land between Ainsworth and Wallula in 1880s as "a preemptive strike."[50] In late 1881 the railroad ran from Wallula about 200 miles to Eight Mile Prairie, Idaho, but it did not build westward from Wallula. By laying track down the south bank of the river from Wallula, Villard had checked the NP's advance toward Portland. Responding to this situation, Billings stressed the town's strategic importance: "The Northern Pacific has always insisted it would build

In the 1880s, rail passengers changing trains at Wallula could step to various businesses. The wooden buildings, typical of emerging towns, were not much improved over those erected during Wallula's earlier years as a riverport. (Jeff Asay, 1991, *Union Pacific Northwest: The Oregon-Washington Railroad & Navigation Company.* Edmonds, Washington, Pacific Fast Mail, p. 37) (California State Railroad Museum Library, Rowlen Collection, negative 32390)

to Wallula even if, from Wallula down, the two companies should build together under Northern Pacific Charter."[51]

Hence, at the site where the new OR&N line connected with Baker's old railroad, the OR&N and the NP both built needed structures. In 1883 Walla Wallan Lewis McMorris – who had once freighted goods from Wallula to Walla Walla – platted the new town, often called Wallula Junction, on the Walla Walla River.[52] Understanding the profound change in transportation, many Wallulans moved to the new Wallula. Its hastily erected wooden business buildings fronting the railroad tracks were scarcely more attractive than those built in the 1860s fronting the Columbia. The *Spokane Times* on June 16, 1881, called Wallula "one of the oldest and certainly the shabbiest town on the Columbia."

In 1881 the ambitious and self-confident Villard had seized control of the NP, forcing it to utilize his OR&N line to Portland. His unanticipated acquisition of the railroad attracted enormous attention. An eastern publication explained that financiers "awoke to the fact that Villard and his friends held a majority of its [Northern Pacific's] stock, and that this great corporation, with its valuable charter and immense land grant, was controlled by a comparatively obscure company, whose operations had hitherto been confined to our remotest shores."[53] Villard's financial maneuver meant that Wallula, not Ainsworth, would have economic importance.

In June 1881, the NP, overcoming a shortage of building materials, a brief strike and village saloons that intoxicated track layers, linked Wallula to Spokane. Meanwhile, the company built a 14-mile, standard-gauge track to replace the 3-foot narrow gauge between Ainsworth and Wallula. During October 1882, 100 Chinese laborers cleared sagebrush at a site near Wallula in preparation for the construction of a roundhouse, turntable, woodsheds and a 52,000-gallon water tank. Late that year workers linked Wallula with Portland and switched from wood- to coal-burning locomotives. In September 1883, Villard presided at a golden spike ceremony completing the Northern Pacific, but transcontinental travelers had to change both trains and companies in remote Wallula. Immigrant car passengers did not transfer but continued in their special coaches. Surely, riders traveling in the 1880s must have expressed surprise while dining in this arid community and switching to OR&N equipment for a 212-mile ride to Portland.

Thus, in the 1880s, railroad officials, passengers and shippers, like similar types in earlier decades, recognized Wallula as a major transportation center. Over time the bateaux, steamboat, wagon, and rail car had brought activity and profits. The locomotive's whistle replaced that of the steamboat and echoed through Wallula Gap. The piercing sound excited residents, especially children.

The NP facilities included an eight-stall roundhouse and car repair sheds. The rail cars are on sidings. Columbia River islands are in the background. (Whitman College and Northwest Archives)

Wallulans boasted about impressive railroad construction, including the Walla Walla River's iron truss bridge that replaced a wooden structure in 1887 and about the NP's hotel with its hardwood floors, engine houses, coal bunkers, machine shops and interchange yard. Residents considered the OR&N depot, measuring 40 feet by 200 feet and built in 1885, as the town's most impressive building. Along with others, they praised the introduction of comfortable Pullman sleeping cars; one of the first four was called the "Wallula."

County directories listed farmers, grocers, hotel keepers, bartenders, lawyers and others seeking prosperity in the second Wallula. Employed by either the NP or OR&N, many trainmen – engineers, firemen, brakemen, repairmen, conductors and wipers – took up residence. Cattlemen and orchardists lived on the city's outskirts. These directories reported that Wallula's population increased from 200 in 1884 to 500 in 1890, numbers that disappointed speculators.[54] Local real estate agents advertised in depots, but few home seekers traveling in immigrant cars purchased property in the dusty rail center. Passengers in the 1880s expressed just about the same negative view of the bleak environment as Oregon Trail travelers had voiced in the 1840s.

Residents of the dreary Wallula Hotel continued to voice complaints. The place received considerable publicity when newspapers published humorist Bill Nye's hotel experience. In the mid-1880s, he changed trains in Wallula and rented a filthy room that smelled of plug tobacco and perspiration. Nye reported he could not sleep owing to "the wail of the damned souls who had formerly stopped at this hotel." They returned "at night and tormented the poor guests by bragging over the superiority of hell as a refuge from the Wallula hotel."[55]

Harper's Magazine in 1882 recognized the region's aridity but acknowledged, "One is astonished to see the immense numbers of farming and harvesting implements and machinery, in all their glory of fresh red and green paint, crowding the boats and trains on their way to the front of civilization." The writer added that crops taxed "the carrying capacity of boats and trains to the utmost."[56] Wallulans handled this incoming machinery and outgoing crops being shipped to and from Walla Walla until the OR&N curtailed steamboat operations.

In 1888 the *Wallula Herald* appeared, a modest weekly newspaper issued by R. Cummins and sons. He was a local physician and surgeon giving special attention to the chronic diseases of women and children. The editor, booster J.M. Cummins, sold real estate and wrote: "Wallula is not having a great big boom, but she is having a steady growth and the day is not far distant when Wallula will be a city of no small dimensions. It is now acknowledged to be the greatest railroad center on the coast."[57] The promoter argued that his town "has more arrival and departure of trains than any other city four times its size in the territory"; furthermore, it had a promising future. Cummins predicted that impressive winter resort hotels would be built for invalids seeking cool breezes. The writer explained: "Wallula is the Indian [word] for many winds, or shifting winds," and these winds contributed to good health and long life "as miasmatic malarial disorders cannot breed in this locality."

A *Herald* advertisement boasted that five railroad lines came into Wallula carrying 15 to 30 trains daily.[58] Three local lines served productive agricultural regions, including Dayton, Pendleton, Lewiston, Pomeroy and Colfax. Maintaining that a huge area paid tribute to Wallula, its promoters encouraged readers to invest in lots, including the Riverside Addition.

The *Herald* applauded the local school, Baptist church, literary societies organized by young adults and the appearance of a noted musician. The editor reasoned: "The coming of the composer and violinist Heine marks an era in Wallula. We are no longer left out by first-class artists as small potatoes, and few in a hill."[59]

While Wallula enjoyed a modicum of culture, it acknowledged unsavory, drunken bums blocking the streets. The local editor urged readers to clear "our town of this notable trash."[60] At about the same time the city marshall reported that 200 tramps camped on the city's outskirts.

Despite the optimism of the editor and the prominent Cummins family – brothers Amos and Gideon had moved their mercantile store from the river – Wallula was declining by 1890. The editor assured on January 3, 1890, that "Wallula was the Railroad Center of the Northwest," but the following week the Cummins family closed the *Herald*, complaining that most residents "were dead heads" because they refused to assist their newspaper.[61]

The *Herald's* death reflected the town's ill health. In 1884 the NP became free of Villard's control, built the town of Pasco and started constructing a line to Puget Sound. In 1887 the Union Pacific (UP) acquired OR&N and the Oregon Short Line – a subsidiary of the UP – and built across the Blue Mountains, into Umatilla and to Portland. These decisions meant that Wallula could not keep pace with Pasco and Umatilla; therefore, in 1889 trainmen relocated. Stories circulated in the Columbia River Valley that in booming Pasco lots sold for as much as $700; meanwhile, Wallulans priced them as low as $22. In fact, all the towns on the recently completed NP line, including Ritzville and Spokane, sought to attract settlers and investors. Offering more promising land, these competitors easily outpaced Wallula.

Just as Wallula was sinking, promoter Walter Lingenfelder hailed the town's prospects in the February 8, 1890, issue of *West Shore.* Sounding like a modern James Vansyckle, he insisted that operating major railroads and the "revival of steamboat navigation" assured prosperity. The booster predicted that a mile below Wallula was a "bridge of rock" that could serve as "substantial foundation for a railroad bridge across the great river." Lingenfelder identified the need of a Wallula flour mill and assured: "Water power can be easily and cheaply furnished by the digging of a water ditch from the Walla Walla River." A woolen mill would also be profitable. He concluded: "The citizens, in the main, are refined, intelligent, and enterprising"; furthermore, they enjoyed "bland, balmy weather, and days of soft, mellow sunshine."

But this belated boosterism failed to attract capitalists. Over time ranchers removed the declining town's deserted buildings – a removal that had also happened after the mining rush ended. In 1887 a visitor assured, "When irrigation redeems the adjacent country from its present unproductive condition, the town will no doubt become an important business point."[62] Such optimism was not realized in the 1890s. At the turn of the century, Wallula – now a village not a rail center – served a cattle and farming community. Its few inhabitants, struggling with aridity and wind, hoped that nearby irrigation projects would revive its ailing economy.

•••

Located at Wallula Gap, the fort and town in the 19th century had played a vital economic role, serving significant individuals and companies that shaped a vast region. American Indians had engaged in a beneficial trade with Fort Walla Walla. During the settlement of the Pacific Northwest, the fort and town had assisted fur trappers and travelers. Because of its pivotal location, Wallula had played a prominent role in the business history of the North West Company, Hudson's Bay Company, Oregon Steam Navigation Company, Walla Walla and Columbia River Railroad, Oregon Railway and Navigation Company, Northern Pacific Railroad and Union Pacific Railroad. British and American leaders exported commodities, especially furs, gold and wheat through Wallula Gap. Promoters, most notably James Vansyckle, Dorsey Baker and the Cummins family; and travelers, especially trappers, missionaries, soldiers, homeseekers and miners, looked to the site as an oasis, transportation center or mercantile outpost. In the 1880s, locomotives pounding through Wallula Gap's desolate walls pierced the solitude. Only a rare motorist passing today's third Wallula, sitting in the sage and sand like its predecessors, comprehends that it had, as historian D.W. Meinig insisted, "a brief but lasting fame."[63]

Endnotes

1. James P. Ronda, *Astoria and Empire* (Lincoln, Nebraska: University of Nebraska Press, Lincoln, 1990), 64.

2. Richard Somerset Mackie, *Trading Beyond the Mountains* (Vancouver: University of British Columbia Press, Vancouver, 1997), 21.

3. Alvin M. Josephy Jr., *The Nez Perce Indians and the Opening of the Northwest* (Boston: Houghton Mifflin Company, 1997), 55.

4. Kenneth A. Spaulding, ed., *Alexander Ross, The Fur Traders of the Far West* (Norman: University of Oklahoma Press, 1956), 119.

5. *George Simpson's 1828 Journey to the Columbia* (London, Hudson's Bay Record Society, 1947), 51.

6. D.W. Meinig, *The Great Columbia Plain* (Seattle: University of Washington Press, 1968), 62.

7. Spaulding, ed., *Alexander Ross*, 145.

8. Quoted in Josephy, *The Nez Perce Indians*, 5.

9. F.G. Young, ed., *The Correspondence and Journals of Captain Nathaniel J. Wyeth, 1831-6* (New York: Arno Press 1973 reprint of 1899 edition),173.

10. Mackie, *Trading Beyond the Mountains*, 104.

11. Quoted in John Phillip Reid, *Contested Empire, Peter Skene Ogden and the Snake River Expeditions* (Norman: University of Oklahoma Press, 2002), 20-31.

12. Charles Wilkes, *Narrative of the United States Exploring Expedition* (Philadelphia: Lea and Blanchard, 1845) v. IV, 292.

13. Jennifer Ott, " 'Ruining' the Rivers in the Snake Country: The Hudson's Bay Company's Fur Desert Policy," *Oregon Historical Quarterly* (Summer 2003), 177-178.

14. Wilkes, *Narrative*, 390.

15. Quoted in Reid, *Contested Empire*, 59.

16. Quoted in Meinig, *Great Columbia Plain*, 84.

17. *Correspondence of Wyeth*, 184.

18. John Kirk Townsend, *Narrative of a Journey Across the Rocky Mountains to the Columbia River* (Fairfield, Washington: Ye Galleon Press, 1970), 281-282.

19. Quoted in Dorothy Nafus Morrison, *Outpost: John McLoughlin and the Far Northwest* (Portland: Oregon Historical Society Press, 1999), 261.

20. Wilkes, *Narrative*, 391.

21. *Correspondence of Wyeth*, 173.

22. Josephy, *The Nez Perce Indians*, 112.

23. Frances Fuller Victor, *The River of the West: The Adventures of Joe Meek* (Missoula: Mountain Press, 1983), v. I, 212.

24. Lawrence Dodd, ed., *Narcissa Prentiss Whitman, My Journal, 1836* (Fairfield, Washington: Ye Galleon Press, 1982), 41. William H. Gray, who traveled with the Whitmans, stated that Pierre Pambrun, chief trader for Hudson's Bay Company, pastured 30 head of the fattest cattle he had ever seen and that "his hogs seem as if they could scarcely move from fatness." He also concluded that the fort's melons were better than any he had "eaten in the states." Archer Butler Hulbert and Dorothy Printup Hulbert (eds.), *Marcus Whitman Crusader* (Colorado College and Denver Public Library, 1936), part 1, 228.

25. Theodore Stern, *Chiefs and Change in the Oregon Country: Indian Relations at Fort Nez Percés, 1818-1855* (Corvallis: Oregon State University Press, 1996) v. 2, 168.

26. Thomas J. Farnham, *An 1839 Wagon Train Journal*, republished by Pacific Northwest National Parks and Forests Association (Monroe, Oregon, 1983), 79.

27. Wilkes, *Narrative*, 390.

28. John Charles Frémont, *Report of the Expedition to the Rocky Mountains*

in the year 1842 and to Oregon and North California in the Years 1834-1844 (Washington: Blair and Rives, 1845), 184.

29. Mackie, *Trading Beyond the Mountains*, 253.

30. Wilkes, *Narrative*, 403.

31. Meinig, *The Great Columbia Plain*, 150.

32. *North American Indians*, v. 7 (Washington: Smithsonian Institution, 1990), 141.

33. Josephy, *The Nez Perces Indians*, 266.

34. G. Thomas Edwards, "Town Boosterism on Oregon's Mining Frontier," *Oregon Historical Quarterly* (Spring 2005), 76-97.

35. G. Thomas Edwards, "Walla Walla Gateway to the Pacific Northwest Interior," *Montana, the Magazine of Western History* (Summer 1990), 28-43.

36. *Walla Walla Statesman*, August 30, 1862.

37. *Walla Walla Statesman*, October 12, 1866.

38. *Walla Walla Statesman*, June 1, 1866.

39. *Oregonian*, July 24, 1862.

40. Theodore Stern, *Chiefs & Chief Traders: Indian Relations at Fort Nez Percés, 1818-1885* (Corvallis: Oregon State University Press, 1993) v. 1, 98.

41. Shirley Ann Wilson Moore, "We Feel the Want of Protection: The Politics of Law and Race in California, 1848-1878," *California History* (Number 3/4, 2003), 105.

42. C. Aubrey Angelo, *Sketches of Travel in Oregon and Idaho* (Fairfield, Washington: Ye Galleon Press, 1988), 38.

43. Arthur L. Throckmorton, *Oregon Argonauts* (Portland: Oregon Historical Society, 1961), 269.

44. *Walla Walla Statesman*, August 24, 1866.

45. *Ibid.*

46. *Walla Walla Statesman*, June 2, 1867.

47. Frances Fuller Victor, *All Over Oregon and Washington* (San Francisco: John M. Carmay and Co., 1872), 104.

48. *Walla Walla Union*, November 27, 1880.

49. *Pacific Semaphore*, 1882, 4-2, F.B. Gill Collection, Oregon Historical Society.

50. Robin Winks, *Frederick Billings: A Life* (New York: Oxford University Press, 1991), 243.

51. *Ibid.* 243.

52. *Walla Walla Union Bulletin*, May 24, 1953.

53. *Harper's Monthly Magazine* (November 1883), 940.

54. *Oregon, Washington, and Idaho Gazetteer and Business Directory, 1884-1885 and 1891-1892* (Portland: R.L. Polk Co., 1884 and 1892), 609 and 1220. In 1882 the Northern Pacific advertised "town property" at Ritzville, Sprague, Cheney, Spokane Falls and other promising locations served by its new line. The advertisement excluded its arid rail centers, Ainsworth and Wallula. Cheney, *Northwest Tribune*, October 20, 1882.

55. *Oregonian*, January 14, 1886; Lewis O. Saum, "Bill Nye in the Pacific Northwest," *Pacific Northwest Quarterly*, July 1983, 82-90.

56. *Harper's Monthly Magazine* (December 1882), 5.

57. *Wallula Weekly Herald*, November 30, 1888.

58. *Ibid.*

59. *Ibid.*

60. *Ibid.*

61. *Wallula Monthly Herald*, January 3 and 10, 1890.

62. "Walla Walla and Vicinity," *The West Shore* (March 1887), 209.

63. Meinig, *Great Columbia Plain*, 480.

McNary Dam, shown under construction in the 1950s, impounds Lake Wallula and is one of four U.S. Army Corps of Engineers dams on the lower Columbia. (Oregon State Archives)

7

History in the 20th Century: "We'll Rise Again"

Lawrence L. Dodd

"No section of the Inland Empire ... has a richer fund of historical facts to draw upon than this old site [Wallula], which was at one time the gateway to the Inland Empire."

–Albert S. Johnson, *Wallula Gateway*, May 31, 1929

Photograph by the Arnold Studio titled "Columbia River Gap." On the back of a black-and-white postcard with this photo is "Wm. DeLong's rowboat." (Fred L. Mitchell Collection) DeLong (1863-1941) was born in Ohio and in 1888, with his wife and two children, came to Wallula by train. In 1936 he was "farming a fertile acreage where the Walla Walla River, a few rods beyond, merges with the Columbia." (*Wallula Gateway*, May 1, 1936). "In the back yard of the DeLong home in Wallula, enough lumber is stacked to build a dozen row boats. The first one was completed a few weeks ago and is named 'White Swan' in tribute to the Indian friend of the same name. ... Mr. DeLong is making these boats to sell. They are 16 feet long with a 40-inch beam. The price complete with oars is only $35." (*Wallula Gateway*, March 17, 1939).

In 1939, Bernice Rice wrote a poem to go with this picture:
The Columbia is singing
Her eternal melody
As she gathers up the rivers
And presents them to the sea.

For the first 53 years of the 20th century, the citizens of Wallula searched for ways to regain their 19th century position of importance and prosperity.

In 1905 the editor of the *Wallula Gateway* predicted "Wallula Will Become a City – Bigger and Better Than Ever." Many residents remembered the boom days when Wallula was an important supply point for towns and mining districts to the north, east and south and later a major railroad town. Although those days had disappeared, Wallula residents were certain they could rekindle the success of earlier times.

Early Property Owners

The man who originally platted the second town of Wallula was viewed as a factor in retarding progress. The *Wallula Gateway* reported Lewis McMorris, owner of a principal part of Wallula real estate, did "absolutely" nothing to improve the town and consequently "has our hands tied." He had trouble selling or leasing his property and "old shacks," and when he did it was at "exorbitant" prices. He would agree to help progress, then back out, and on inspection trips he would bemoan the fact that his property did not increase in value.

This was in direct contrast to Sam Ash (1856-1928) who had arrived in Wallula in 1877, at the age of 21. Throughout his 51 years in Wallula, Ash gained the reputation that would characterize him: "Without brag or show of selfishness he went his way doing good," wrote J.C. Julian, the publisher of the *Wallula Gateway*. Upon arrival Ash became involved in the sheep industry, investing his income by increasing his flock, purchasing land in Wallula, Clover

Left: Lewis McMorris, 1831-1915. Owning land east of the original town of Wallula, McMorris took advantage of the arrival of the railroad by donating land for a depot. In 1883 he platted the second town of Wallula. In 1908 the *Wallula Gateway* reported that McMorris still owned a "principal part of Wallula real estate." (W.D. Lyman, 1901, *An Illustrated History of Walla Walla County*, facing p. 320)

Below: Front Street, Wallula. (Whitman College and Northwest Archives) "The town had a street along the railroad four or five blocks long. ... Going south from the livery stable was the Wallula Hotel. ... Next in that block were a grocery store, a building used for a bank, a general merchandise store, a Chinese restaurant and a saloon. ... There was a wooden sidewalk which ran in front of those buildings and the street was six or eight feet below the sidewalk with a stairway running from the street to the sidewalk. ... This was the main business district of the town. There was a good space there between the railroad tracks and the store and Mr. Ash used to ship in lumber and pile it down there to sell." (Cecil S.G. Cummings, 1978, *My Life in the Walla Walla Valley*, p. 17.)

and Horse Heaven Hills and various regional investments. In 1891 he established a saloon in Wallula and by 1898 had established a mercantile store that became a very successful business. Later he also owned and operated a confectionary and pool hall.

Although starting with little capital, his careful management of funds, good investments and successful business ventures allowed him to accumulate a small fortune, which he spent improving Wallula and supporting its residents. The *Wallula Gateway* reported that at Christmastime he was known to give "down and outers" a dollar with the greeting, "Boys, this is Christmas. Spend this for a good, hot dinner today." This was only one of many acts of charity credited to Ash. He was a one-man commercial club, dedicating his resources to support his community and its residents.

Weather Extremes

Wallula was known for its extremes in the weather, which could impede commerce at various times throughout the year. In February 1907, a chinook wind brought disaster to the area. Miles of railroad track, roads and many bridges were destroyed, and Wallula, with its five railroads, was cut off from the outside world. In the winter, travel on the Columbia River could cease due to large chunks of floating ice or it being entirely frozen. When the temperature was extremely low for a long time and the Columbia River froze and river traffic ceased, the frozen rivers did furnish ice for those who stored ice for the summer months. Sam Ash was reported as having a crew sawing ice at Nine Mile and storing it in his icehouse near his mercantile store.

Donald Church wrote that 1915-16 was the severest winter

he had experienced at Wallula. His father operated a ferry across the river, and the family lived a short distance away. He remembered that the temperature reached 23 degrees below zero with 30 inches of snow. The ice on the Wallula side of the Columbia River was at least a foot thick, and when the ice began to break up, it created a dam in the rapids near the mouth of the Walla Walla River. As the river rose, the ice broke into chunks an estimated 3 to 20 feet across, "piling up on our shore maybe 10 feet or so above the former level, and smashing anything in its path." Later the ice broke up a second time and piled more blocks of ice even higher on the shore. It took considerable time for the river to clear of drifting ice blocks and to resume safe river transportation.

Twenty years later the *Wallula Gateway* reported that spring the Columbia River was full of ice. So much ice was floating downstream that a family living on a small island near the west shore found the only way to reach work on the east shore was to become "ice cake jumpers."

In direct contrast many summers were extremely hot, and the water level in the Columbia River could fall too low to bring steamboats safely to Wallula. The heat and wind made many summer days uncomfortable. One former resident wrote, "I once endured the gentle zephyrs and sandstorms of that dilapidated old town."

Introduction of Irrigation

An early attempt to rekindle Wallula's importance was the movement to establish irrigation tracts on the arid lands around Wallula. In 1891, a dam was proposed on the Walla Walla River a mile south of the Nine Mile Bridge (at Reese). The proposal was to transport

water from a dam through a gravity-fed ditch to agricultural land being platted to the north of Wallula. Upon approval, a concrete dam 155 feet long, 11.5 feet wide and 20 feet high was constructed. The reservoir furnished water to an open ditch 14 feet wide at the bottom, 32 feet wide at the top and 6 feet deep. The canal was completed in 1906 and was at least 12 miles long, feeding some 15 miles of lateral ditches. This project stimulated the establishment of two new communities to the north of Wallula: Attalia and Two Rivers, both of which rapidly grew and created business ventures that challenged Wallula.

The Attalia Irrigation Company built a concrete dam south of Nine Mile (Reese) on the Walla Walla River to supply water to lands in the Wallula and Attalia area. The canal followed the south side of the Walla Walla River some 3.5 miles to a site east of Three Mile School. Here it crossed the Walla Walla River, following the north side of the river for another two miles, then north to the Attalia area. (Attalia Commercial Club pamphlet)

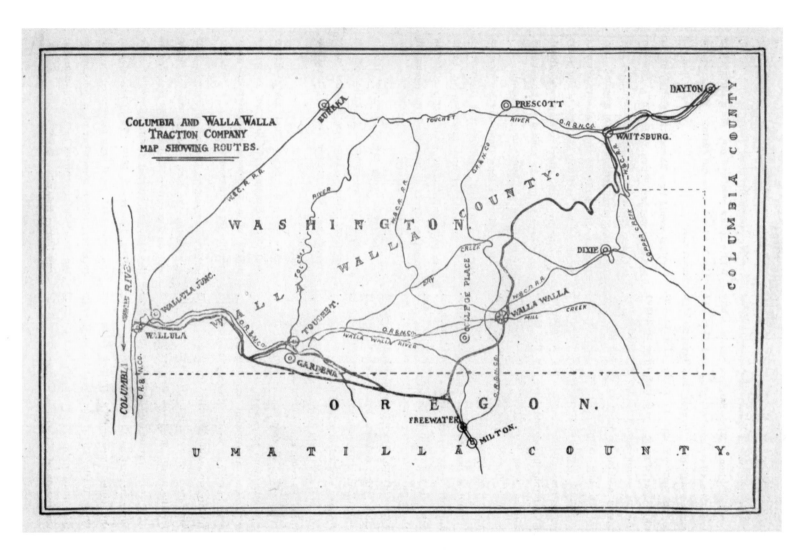

This map for the proposed Walla Walla Traction Company was published in *Up-to-the-Times Magazine*, Volume 1, No. 2, December 1906, page 10.

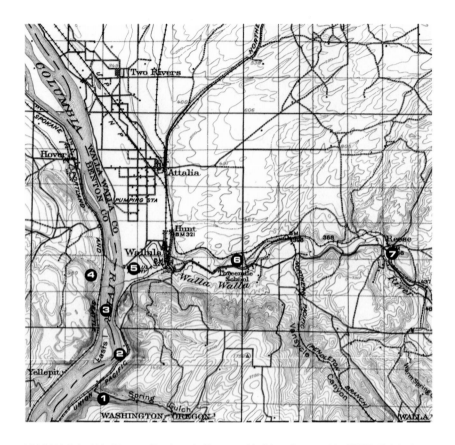

1918 Wallula, Washington Quadrangle Topographic Map. Surveyed in 1915. Original scale 1:125,000 (each small square is a section, equal to one square mile). Note the many islands in the Columbia River, and the location of:
1. Port Kelley
2. Thrasher Ranch
3. Twin Sisters
4. Columbia River Bird Refuge (two small islands)
5. Site of Fort Nez Perce (Walla Walla); first town of Wallula and ferry landing
6. Attalia Irrigation Company Dam flume across Walla Walla River
7. Attalia Irrigation Company concrete dam

Proposed Traction Company

While the irrigation project progressed and land was cultivated, a new opportunity to stimulate Wallula's economy developed. The Walla Walla Traction Company (electric line) planned to build a line from Dayton to Wallula. Also, the Columbia and Walla Walla Traction Company, in cooperation with the Graves Line, was considering a traction line from Spokane through the Palouse country to Walla Walla and on to Wallula. Wallula could become a major import and export center, a supply point for many communities in Eastern Washington, and a terminus for products being shipped out of the Inland Empire.

Railroad Lines In and Out of Wallula

In 1908, the *Up-to-the-Times Magazine* reported that five railroad lines passed through Wallula: the main Oregon Railroad & Navigation line from Portland to Spokane, with a branch to Walla Walla; Northern Pacific from Palouse; Washington & Columbia River Railroad connecting to the Oregon Short Line at Pendleton; Washington & Columbia River Railroad to Walla Walla and Dayton; and across the river the North Bank road, which gave another outlet via the Great Northern system. With all the railroads in the vicinity, it was predicted that Wallula would "become one of the great wheat shipping centers of Eastern Washington," and the traction lines would help support that prediction. The traction lines might also break the monopoly held by the Oregon Railroad & Navigation Company. In 1907, the *Wallula Gateway* reported that Oregon Railroad & Navigation Company patrons would gladly return to the "good old freighting days when mules and oxen were the motive power." The company had a reputation for damaging freight, making only partial deliveries and responding slowly to claims, if they responded at all.

For several years the residents of Wallula hoped at least one traction line would reach their community, but the idea did not materialize.

Flour Mill

Toward the end of 1907, W.R. Butler, president-secretary, and J.W. Seeley, treasurer-manager, proposed construction of the Wallula Flour Mills to receive the 1909 wheat crop. It took over a year before sufficient support was obtained to start the project. On March 22, 1909, the machinery had been ordered, and teams and scrapers began excavating the foundation. The plans specified a building 32 feet by 54 feet, a solid concrete foundation, a boiler and fuel house measuring 30 feet by 40 feet, with future plans to construct storage warehouses and a feed mill. However, by the end of the year Butler had moved from Wallula, and the *Wallula Gateway* reported that Butler "made strenuous efforts to erect a mill here, with something more tangible than hot air, but he failed as do all such promoters."

Fire a Serious Threat

In 1908, Wallula boasted a population of 250 residents, two churches, three schoolteachers, three stores, two saloons, an opera house, several restaurants and lodging houses, several railroads, and a newspaper. In mid-October the Oregon Railroad & Navigation depot was destroyed by fire. It was feared Wallula would be destroyed, but when the wind subsided, the local residents were able to control the fire and save the town. The event prompted Sam Ash to order a 3,000-gallon water tank with hose, increase the depth of his well, and install a gas engine to improve filling his water tank, all in the hopes of controlling future town fires.

Expansion and Changes of Railroad Facilities

When the new Oregon Railroad & Navigation (OR&N) depot was expanded to accommodate all railroad lines coming into Wallula, the *Wallula Gateway* reported that the railroads "promised several other improvements – repair shops, roundhouse, stockyards, etc." The OR&N did erect a coal platform with 14 iron buckets, each holding 1,000 pounds of coal. It also built a new stockyard to handle the needs of livestock being moved through Wallula by rail. By September of 1910, blueprints had been drawn for 13 new sidetracks. With the announced consolidation of the OR&N and the North Coast railroads, Wallula was speculating that it would again be placed "on the map." The OR&N approached Wallula from all directions, "making it a logical diversion point," and the considerable funds invested in railroad improvements seemed sufficient evidence that machine shops and a roundhouse would soon be located in Wallula.

Another rumor claimed that the Northern Pacific officials might build a bridge across the Columbia River, "on the rocks," near the mouth of the Walla Walla River, making Wallula "The Hub" of the railroads.

By 1915, the Oregon-Washington Railroad and Navigation

Company had decided to move offices from North Yakima and Starbuck to Walla Walla, where they planned to invest some $30,000 constructing a 10-stall roundhouse and auxiliary machine shop. Even so, in 1916, when surveyors from the Oregon-Washington Railroad and Navigation Company spent time giving Wallula the "once over," the citizens again dreamed that a roundhouse, railway yards and machine shops would soon be built in their community.

Prospects of Wallula Becoming Major River Port

In 1908, the Open River Transportation Company began building two steamboats at Celilo. Wallulans saw prospects of becoming a major river port, but the steamboats *Inland Empire* and later the *Twin Cities* utilized port facilities at Pasco and Kennewick and bypassed Wallula. In 1915, the Port of Kennewick was created; its builders claimed they had invested $7,000 in docks in the best natural harbor on the Columbia River. Pasco followed the same line of development, and such ports were necessary as both communities grew.

Even with the development of port facilities within 17 miles of Wallula, Walla Walla Valley residents viewed the opening of The Dalles-Celilo Canal as a renewed opportunity for establishing a port at Wallula. Announcing the opening program of The Dalles-Celilo Canal, the *Walla Walla Evening Bulletin* reported, "Thousands Witness Arrival of Fleet at Wallula." On May 4, 1915, people from all sections of southeastern Washington arrived at Wallula by automobile and railroad to join in the pageantry planned for this monumental event. An estimated 5,000 people gathered to meet the "fleet" that started at Lewiston, stopping at various ports of call on their way to Portland. The steamers, carrying governors, United States senators, representatives and prominent citizens arrived at the site of old Fort Nez Perce (Walla Walla) in the afternoon, led by the flagship *Undine*. The paper reported, "The Wallula country never appeared to better advantage," and residents were encouraged that the opening of The Dalles-Celilo Canal would stimulate interest in developing a port at Wallula. Professor William D. Lyman, Northwest historian, speaker at the Wallula celebration, commented: "We may well ask ourselves what is … the large and permanent significance of this event. I find two special meanings in it, one commercial and industrial, the other patriotic and political. First, it is the establishment of water transportation and waterpower in the Columbia Basin on a scale never before known. Do we yet

The *Bertha*, 1915, Wallula Landing. Built by W.D. Church in about 1914, the *Bertha* was a sternwheeler catamaran ferry. Over the years several individuals operated a ferry at Wallula. In 1908 the *Wallula Gateway* reported that the *Elsie May*, owned by Robert Pitman, would cross the Columbia River in seven minutes. Church purchased the *Elsie May* but found the ferry in very poor condition, so he built the *Bertha*. (Church Collection, Whitman College and Northwest Archives)

Opening of The Dalles-Celilo Canal Celebration, Wallula, May 4, 1915. People "from all parts of Walla Walla County … and … surrounding towns, assembled on the shores of the Columbia River, at the site of the historic old Fort Walla Walla, near Wallula and celebrated in appropriate manner. " (*Up-to-the-Times Magazine*, June 1915, p. 6442-6443)

A. Looking downstream, showing the ferry headquarters building, Wallula Gap and the Twin Sisters. **B.** Flagship *Undine* at the Wallula ferry landing. **C.** Crowd around the "Merchant House," view looking upstream. (Fred Mitchell Collection)

Looking upstream at the crowd gathered for the Open River Celebration. The lone man on the right is standing on the adobe foundation of Fort Walla Walla. D.B. Church wrote, "The only house remaining then was the 'Merchants' house, somewhat up-river from ours." (Whitman College and Northwest Archives)

comprehend what this may mean to us and [our] descendants in this vast and productive land?"

Improved River Crossing Impacts Establishing a Port at Wallula

Prior to 1921, access from Walla Walla County to the west side of the Columbia and Snake rivers was by ferry. Over the years, ferries had been located at Wallula, Attalia and Burbank; access to the west side was slow and inconvenient. In the summer of 1918, the *Walla Walla Union* reported, "Automobile travel is now at its height, and drivers many times have to wait for hours to get across the river." When ports were established in Pasco and Kennewick the need for a convenient Walla Walla County port facility at Wallula was again discussed. The improvement of roads between Wallula and Burbank and the opening of the Snake River Bridge (April 15, 1921) furnished easy access to Pasco and Kennewick ports, railroad facilities and the two growing communities. Again a port at Wallula failed to materialize.

Ice Plant

By mid-1915 the Pacific Fruit Express Company, a subsidiary of the Union Pacific and Southern Pacific and the world's largest refrigerator car operation for the transportation of perishable freight, established a $25,000 icehouse at Wallula. Ice was delivered by rail from various ice-producing plants owned by the company. The plant could store 6,000 to 7,000 tons of ice for refrigerator fruit cars arriving from the Milton-Freewater and Walla Walla fruit-producing districts. In 1918 an addition increased the capacity to 10,000

Incline conveyor and 15-car-length icing platform with ice manufacturing plant in background. On the south side of the ice plant and the west side of the icing platform were some 10 structures, including office, shop and storage buildings. Attached to the southwest corner of the ice plant were the pump room, snake-type ammonia condenser stand and shelter, compressor room with two Vilter horizontal ammonia compressors and storage room. North of the ice plant were located the plant manager's cottage and garage, circa 1949. (Courtesy California State Railroad Museum)

tons to accommodate additional fruit cars from the Yakima Valley. Two years later the company expanded the plant by installing ice-manufacturing equipment that could produce 55 tons of ice daily. The plant, during the busy season, would pack 400 tons of ice in approximately 65 refrigerator cars every 24 hours. The icing deck was long enough to ice 15 cars at a time, normally requiring 20 minutes. Crews worked 24 hours a day, and between 11 p.m. and 4 a.m., they had to switch Northern Pacific passenger cars, while still keeping up with icing. The crew also did light inspection, cleaning and minor repairs on the cars. During the busy season, 100 tons of additional ice was shipped in from Portland, Spokane and North Powder ice plants. During the off-season the plant built up its stockpile of ice, and the crew serviced refrigerator cars with charcoal burners, suited to keep fruit from freezing when trains passed through very cold regions.

It took 40 to 50 men to operate the plant 24 hours a day at the peak of the season, 10 or 12 in the slack season. Since a number of the employees were transient, the company provided a reading room, showers, bath and toilet facilities, a library, eating facilities, and sleeping quarters. The plant continued to expand and became a landmark at Wallula, until it was acquired by the U.S. government and sold as salvage by the Corps of Engineers in 1953.

River Recreational Facilities

While Wallula residents sought ways to become the "gateway" to the Inland Empire, sporting clubs in Walla Walla looked at ways to improve the beachfront along the Columbia River. In 1923, the newly organized Walla Walla Bass Club built a concrete clubhouse on the site of the original Fort Nez Perce (Walla Walla), containing a kitchen, a small meeting space, and room for a boat. In 1926, the Walla Walla Sportsmen's Association tried to acquire 200 acres of land along the shoreline for a state park. The plan, to be funded through donations, was to raise sufficient monies to purchase the property and turn it over to the Washington State Parks Department. In 1928, the Sportsmen's Association hosted a picnic to support the state park idea, and more than 150 automobiles arrived with supporters. In conjunction with the proposed construction of

Wallula "from atop south end of ice plant." On the left is the south end of the icing platform for 15 refrigerator cars, and beyond that is part of the railroad yard, the water tower and the Wallula Hotel, as seen on May 24, 1949. (Courtesy California State Railroad Museum)

In 1923 a concrete boathouse (foreground) was built on the southwest corner of the site of the adobe (third) Fort Walla Walla. To the south are Wallula Gap and the Twin Sisters. (L.L. Dodd Collection)

Circa 1930, a larger concrete boathouse was built on the southwest corner of the second Fort Walla Walla. For 14 weeks during 1949-50, Thomas R. Garth, National Park Service archaeologist, conducted a salvage dig of Fort Walla Walla. This site was also the location of the first town of Wallula, a ferry landing and a port for early river traffic. (Fred L. Mitchell Collection)

the Wallula-Umatilla Cut-Off, the park was promoted as a way to attract "hundreds of tourists" and campers to help support Wallula economy. By 1931, the Walla Walla County commissioners decided not to sell county-owned, riverfront property, and private landowners had doubled their price, bringing the Sportsman's Association proposal to an end.

Bird Refuge Established

On August 28, 1926, President Calvin Coolidge, through Executive Order No. 4501, set aside two small islands west of Wallula "for the use of the Department of Agriculture as a refuge and breeding ground for native birds." The two islands, located about one mile each way from the mouth of the Walla Walla River, and comprising 8.23 acres, were designated as the "Columbia River Bird Refuge." Two years later it was discovered that the islands were the property of the Northern Pacific Railway Company, but as the islands had no "recognized economic value," the railroad company deeded the islands to the "government for bird refuge purposes." In 1952, after 26 years as a refuge, the islands were inundated by the impoundment created by McNary Dam. Through another executive order, the existence of the Columbia River Bird Refuge was revoked.

Highway Construction and Improvement

In December 1922, residents of Wallula met at the schoolhouse to discuss constructing a passable road from Wallula to Umatilla. Such a road would help Wallula grow and give Walla Walla Valley residents easier access to Oregon communities to the west.

Late in October 1927, six Wallula men took it upon themselves to start repairing the old wagon road that went through the valley east of the Twin Sisters, hoping this move would inspire the state of Washington to construct a permanent road through the Wallula Gap. Also, this local group met with residents of Hermiston who wanted a road along the Columbia River from Wallula to Umatilla. The idea received little outside interest, although some residents of Pendleton, Oregon, objected to the proposed road, which they believed would divert traffic away from their city and adversely impact their economy.

Although Oregon and Washington State Highway departments showed little interest, representatives from Umatilla, Portland, Seattle and Walla Walla formed a company that proposed to build a toll road that it would sell at cost if the two states wished to take ownership. In September 1928, the Oregon State Highway Committee's attorney claimed the road as "a part of the designated state highway system as well as part of the federal system and as such must be maintained free, so no franchise can be granted for a toll road."

As the idea for a toll road was being considered, a group of residents from Touchet, Pasco, Walla Walla, Wallula and Pendleton met July 29, 1928, at the Modern Woodmen Hall in Wallula to organize the Wallula-Umatilla Cut-Off Association. This organization urged the Washington and Oregon State Highway departments to construct this proposed highway.

The month after formation, H.H. Thrasher, secretary-treasurer of the association, presented the idea to the Eastern Washington Good Roads Association, which endorsed the idea as an extension of State Highway 3. The Cut-Off Association spent the next five years seeking the support of residents of the Inland Empire, local, regional, state and federal agencies, succeeding in October 1930, when the Washington State Highway engineers established temporary headquarters in Wallula and began working on plans for the Wallula-Umatilla Cut-Off, along with highway improvements from Nine Mile Bridge to Wallula.

The engineers first planned the highway to cross the Walla Walla River at the Three Mile Bridge, which had been badly damaged by a fire in 1926, requiring traffic to ford the Walla Walla River until the bridge was repaired. But due to flooding in January 1928, the western approach caved in, 60 feet of the bridge washed out and a pier settled 16 inches. If this bridge were maintained as a crossing for the main highway, then the highway would again have to cross the Walla Walla River south of Wallula a second time to access the proposed cut-off highway. The engineers decided to abandon the Three Mile Bridge and roadway to build a new highway from Vansycle Canyon west. The new road would follow the south side of the Walla Walla River to a site directly south of Wallula, where the highway would cross a newly proposed bridge, and the new stretch of highway would align with the proposed Wallula-Umatilla Cut-Off.

Early in March 1932, Washington and Oregon highway officials met at Umatilla to review the proposed Cut-Off route.

Shortly thereafter, both states began the construction of their respective portions of this new highway.

The old county wooden wagon bridge was replaced, and on Sunday, April 17, 1932, the new bridge over the Walla Walla River was dedicated. The Washington state director of highways approved the proposal submitted by the Walla Walla Chamber of Commerce to dedicate the bridge in honor of Madame Dorion. Madame Marie L'Aguiroise Dorion (1786-1850), member of the Iowa Tribe, was the second woman to come west overland. With her husband and children, she traveled west with the W.P. Hunt party, arriving in the Wallula Gap area in January 1812.

Sunday, July 9, 1933, the Wallula-Umatilla Cut-Off road opened for traffic. It was officially dedicated on September 4. The program, sponsored by the Wallula-Umatilla Cut-Off Association, was held at "Thrasher's Grove" where more than 3,000 people attended a baseball game, picnic and dedication ceremonies.

Thrasher Ranch Fruit

Thrasher's Grove was located about three miles below Wallula, on the east side of the Columbia where the river makes a bend to the west. Thrasher Ranch, also known as Thrasher Gardens, was established before the turn of the 20th century and became known as one of the "finest fruit farms in the west." High bluffs to the east sheltered the site from hard winds, as well as early and late frosts, so trees bore fruit earlier than other orchards in the area. The completion of the Wallula-Umatilla Cut Off was of major benefit to the Thrasher Ranch, for it allowed easy shipment of their produce to market.

Thrasher Ranch and Port Kelley. The Thrasher Ranch was five miles south of Wallula on the Columbia River.

A. The Columbia River at low water. Note the peach orchard between the Thrasher home and the Lombardy poplar trees near Port Kelley. (Fred L. Mitchell Collection) "Resting in a valley at the foot of giant cliffs, the ranch is sheltered from heavy winds, and early and late frosts. The soil is 30 feet deep, and has never been fertilized." (*Wallula Gateway*, April 8, 1931) On September 4, 1933, "A crowd of more than 3,000 persons was present at Thrasher's Grove ... to witness the official dedication of the Wallula-Umatilla Cut-off." (*Wallula Gateway*, September 8, 1933)

B. Southwest of the Thrasher Ranch is Port Kelley. In June 1938 the Walla Walla Grain Growers built an elevator at Port Kelley. Eugene Kelley (1883-1949) was manager of the Walla Walla Grain Growers from 1931 to 1945 and championed the idea of shipping bulk wheat down the Columbia River. In February 1939 the first barge was loaded, and later the barge loading plant was named in honor of Kelley. In May 1939 Clarence Braden was building an elevator at the same site. Two months later the elevators had a capacity of 40,000 bushels of grain. This was an ideal site to load grain barges and is still an important shipping point for bulk grain. (Armstrong Collection, Whitman College and Northwest Archives)

C. The Columbia River flood of late May to early July 1948, the largest since the 1894 flood-of-record. (Fred L. Mitchell Collection)

Navigation Center Being Proposed

Shortly after the cut-off roadway was opened, the Columbia Valley Development League, a Portland organization, proposed dredging a 7-foot-deep, 50-foot-wide river channel from the Celilo Canal to Wallula, making Wallula a navigation center. The company's executive vice president visited Wallula and revealed plans to construct a floating dock and warehouses. The *Wallula Gateway* encouraged residents to advertise the natural advantages of Wallula and promote the town as the "Key to the Inland Empire."

Two years later, the Inland Navigation Company planned to introduce barge traffic on the Columbia River to serve Portland, Vancouver, Hood River, Wallula, Pasco, Kennewick, Riparia and Lewiston. As the Columbia River had not been dredged for deep-draft vessels, the new company planned to introduce low-draft tugs, using the river to transport barges upstream when water conditions permitted. The company realized that it would not be many more years before the government would construct dams on the Columbia and Snake rivers, making possible safe, year-round barge traffic.

By the end of 1936, the company had the first of a proposed six, shallow-draft tugs constructed and heading for the Columbia River. They also had constructed two 55,000-gallon fuel storage tanks, but instead of Wallula, the company chose a site to the north near Attalia.

Lake Wallula Inundates Significant Sites

In the end, water covered Wallula. In July 1923, four members of a U.S. survey team were in Wallula studying how much land would be covered with water if the Umatilla Rapids Dam project were constructed. The study concluded that the backwater would submerge the railroad tracks at Wallula and Attalia, and the proposed pool elevation would be 310.5 feet.

The fate of the aspiring Gateway to the Inland Empire was finally decided in 1953 when the U.S. Army Corps of Engineers completed McNary Dam. This project inundated the site of Fort Nez Perce (Walla Walla) that had played a major role in the Northwest fur trade. It covered the townsite that had been an important supply point for Walla Walla and interior gold mining districts. And it covered the second Wallula that at one time had been a major

railroad point and whose residents had continued to struggle to regain earlier dominance.

Even so, many citizens of Wallula would not allow their community to die, instead electing to move their town to higher ground. Today, Wallula, only a remnant of its past, sits on a rise, on the east side of Highway 12, looking over Lake Wallula, a watery blanket covering the town that played a major role in the history of Walla Walla County.

Hotel Wallula, built about 1890 by W.M. Ellingsworth, was a noted Wallula business. As times changed, half of the building housed, at various times, a store, confectionary, bakery, candy shop and the U. P. Club (tavern). Empty for a number of years, it became a haven for transients needing shelter. Destined to be torn down, it caught fire about midnight, July 30, 1950, and burned down. (Whitman College and Northwest Archives)

Between the town of Wallula and the Columbia River are U.S. Highway 12 and railroad tracks. Beyond the town are the lower Walla Walla River, its delta in Lake Wallula, and the fault scarp along the Olympic-Wallowa lineament. (Bob Carson photo)

Bibliography

Attalia Commercial Club, no date, Attalia on the Columbia: Attalia, Washington.

Bramhall, Marguerite, LaVerne Ruby Kralman, and MaryAnn Little, 1951, Wallula, Washington, "The boom town that never boomed": Whitman College history paper.

Church, Donald B., no date, Recollections: Northwest and Whitman College Archives, Whitman College.

Clarke, E.S., 1897, *Map of the County of Walla Walla.*

Cummings, Bernice, 1988, *History of the three Wallulas*, 1811-1988 (privately printed).

Cummings, Cecil S.G., 1978, *My life in the Walla Walla Valley*: Walla Walla, Washington, General Printing Co.

Garth, Thomas R., 1952, "Archeological excavations at Fort Walla Walla": *Pacific Northwest Quarterly*, p. 27-50.

Lyman, W.D., 1918, *Lyman's history of old Walla Walla County*: Chicago, The S. J. Clarke Publishing Company (two volumes).

Meinig, D.W., 1968, *The Great Columbia Plain: A historical geography, 1805-1910*: Seattle, University of Washington Press.

Ogle, George A., 1909, *Standard atlas of Walla Walla County, Washington*: Chicago, George A. Ogle & Company.

Periodicals

Up-to-the-Times Magazine, Illustrated Monthly: Walla Walla Publishing Company, 1906-28.

Wallula Gateway, 1907-42.

Walla Walla Union, Walla Walla Bulletin, Walla Walla Union-Bulletin, 1900-54.

View northeast across Lake Wallula from above Yellepit. Grain elevators are at the mouth of the Walla Walla River, and wind turbines crown Horse Heaven Hills. (John Clement photo)

8

Conclusion:
Wallula as a Gateway

Robert J. Carson

"This river is remarkably clear and crowded with salmon in many places. ... The bottom can be seen at the depth of 20 feet."
–William Clark, October 17, 1805, *The Definitive Journals of Lewis & Clark*

Natural History

Twenty million years ago, there was no Wallula, no gateway. The low-elevation-but-hilly landscape was underlain by Precambrian quartzite, late Mesozoic granite and early Tertiary volcaniclastics (consolidated or unconsolidated sediments derived from volcanoes). Beginning 16 million years ago, the area was inundated by the Columbia River basalts. The greatest volume of the lava was erupted early and generally flowed west or northwest, more or less perpendicular to the orientation of today's Wallula Gap.

But some of the later flows followed the valley of the Clearwater-Salmon River. Long before the Columbia and Snake rivers came to Wallula, the Clearwater-Salmon was the first gateway, a route for lava to follow from eastern fissures to western lava lakes. Each flow partially or completely filled the valley, forcing the river to cut a new route nearby.

After the last Columbia River basalt followed the valley of the Clearwater-Salmon River 6 million years ago, the river was free to capture other rivers, greatly enlarging its drainage basin to include most of the Pacific Northwest. Its job was not easy, for the anticline of the Horse Heaven Hills was rising, trying to defeat the drainage across it. The anticline rose higher and faster to the west, slowing the mighty Columbia River, and making it easier for the Clearwater-Salmon to capture the Columbia. It was like "Jack and the Beanstalk": The Clearwater-Salmon was Jack, the Columbia was the giant, and the growing Horse Heaven Hills were the beanstalk helping Jack get to the giant. The Clearwater-Salmon extended from its original drainage basin of central Idaho to British Columbia and northern Washington. Next, the combined Clearwater-Salmon-

Columbia River took on the Snake River, a capture resulting in mile-and-a-half-deep Hells Canyon and a drainage basin addition of northwestern Wyoming and southern Idaho. Little Wallula Gap became the gateway for most of the runoff in the Pacific Northwest.

As the Horse Heaven Hills continued to rise, the river kept pace, so that today cliffs up to 1,000 feet high border Wallula Gap. As the gap became deeper, it became more and more a gateway for the wind, particularly because it is aligned with the Prevailing Westerlies.

Since its formation, Wallula Gap has been a gateway for the movement of wildlife. Animals and plants that lived in the warmer, wetter climate of the Miocene more than 5 million years ago would not survive in today's Columbia desert. The fauna and flora have

Viewed from high on the west side of Wallula Gap, the Columbia River and its predecessors have incised deeply into the Horse Heaven Hills as the basalt flows have been uplifted from near sea level. (Bob Carson photo)

transformed almost entirely, not only because of climate change, but also because of evolution, and human-caused extinctions and introductions. What species are left from the Miocene? Perhaps the sturgeon of the deeper, slower parts of the rivers-turned-reservoirs, perhaps the mosses of the cryptobiotic soils. Many organisms migrated over the Horse Heaven Hills; some, like fish and wetland plants, spread along the Columbia River.

During the Pleistocene Ice Age, Wallula became the bottleneck for floods with discharges greater than the flows of all the Earth's rivers combined. The floods through Wallula Gap from Montana's ice-dammed Lake Missoula were fast, brief and frequent. No life below the flood level of about 1,200 feet survived. Between floods, some species of grasses and flowers colonized; they attracted insects, rodents and birds, which in turn attracted carnivores. The next flood flushed this life to the Pacific Ocean, but the organisms returned, again and again.

Human History

Ancient humans may have used Wallula Gap as a gateway and may have camped at Wallula before the last flood about 12,700 years ago. If so, those along the rivers undoubtedly perished in the deluges. The end of the Missoula floods was perhaps Wallula's greatest opportunity to be a gateway. Up the Columbia came steelhead, different species of salmon, and lamprey. These anadromous fish were in tune with the seasonal changes of the great river system, with the variations in discharge and temperature, and with their predators, such as bears, river otters and American Indians. Upstream through Wallula Gap came the pioneering fish; downstream through the gateway went their offspring to the ocean, to return years later. And so the cycles went: downstream and upstream; winter,

Basalt cliffs; sagebrush, grasses and wildflowers; and the west shore of Lake Wallula. (Bob Carson photo)

William Clark's drawing of a salmon. (Reproduced with permission from Missouri History Museum.)

spring, summer and fall; life and death.

The number of salmon migrating up the Columbia has decreased from more than 10 million per year in the 19th century to perhaps 1 million per year today. The potential causes of this decline have been studied and debated for decades. Factors include habitat loss and degradation, overharvest, competition between wild and hatchery fish, and pollutants including heat, sediment, fertilizers and pesticides. Certainly the dams have been a major factor, because the construction of dams too high for fish ladders has cut off about half of the Columbia River drainage basin to fish irrigation: Grand Coulee Dam on the upper Columbia, Dworshak Dam on the North

This pre-dam photo was taken atop the northern basalt cliff on the east side of Wallula Gap. The Columbia River has many islands and channels at low water. In the foreground is a dune field; behind it are small islands of basalt bedrock. From near to far on the east side of the Columbia River are: the mouth of the Walla Walla River; two boat-houses where Fort Walla Walla used to be; and four fuel tanks at Attalia. (Fred L. Mitchell Collection)

Fork of the Clearwater and Hells Canyon Dam on the Snake. What these dams needed were fish elevators! What about lower dams? Most controversial are the four Snake River dams between Wallula and the mouth of the Clearwater River. Improvements for adult and juvenile fish passage have been made. Will this be sufficient, or should these four dams be breached?

Wallula Gap was also a gateway for American Indian travel. The American Indians drifted downriver through the gap, and were strong enough to paddle up current. Perhaps it was easier to walk over the Horse Heaven Hills than to walk along the Columbia River. Walking along the floodplain would have been particularly difficult when the water level was high or where the river meandered against a cliff. However, the river, floodplain and side canyons at Wallula Gap probably provided more food than did a route over the Horse Heaven Hills.

Sacagawea and other American Indians were guides for the European and American explorers and early businessmen. The original human inhabitants showed trappers and explorers the river and land routes, the places like Wallula. The American Indians accompanied Wallula Gap travelers Meriwether Lewis, William Clark, David Thompson and David Douglas. Marcus and Narcissa Whitman stayed at Wallula before moving east to the Walla Walla area.

For thousands of years, Wallula has been on a route of exchange of goods between coastal and inland American Indians. As their populations dwindled due to disease, starvation and murder, the commerce at Wallula did not slacken. Indeed, for two centuries Wallula has been a major commercial gateway in the Pacific Northwest. The trappers went downriver with millions of beaver pelts. The miners came upriver with their equipment: Some stayed in

David Manuel's painting of the confluence of the Walla Walla and Columbia rivers depicts an American Indian from the village at the mouth of the Walla Walla River above Wallula Gap. The steamer *George Wright* heads for Fort Walla Walla. (Fred L. Mitchell Collection with permission from the Manuel family, Hot Lake Springs, LaGrande, Oregon)

northeastern Washington, Idaho and northeastern Oregon; some went home with gold; some went home broke; some died.

Because the miners and others needed meat, many ranchers came through Wallula, bringing sheep and cattle; they killed wolves and other predators. The export of food is important to the economy of the Wallula area. Wallula is home to meat production; a meat-packing plant is adjacent to an enormous feedlot. Fresh produce is rushed by rail from Wallula to eastern United States.

The wood products industry also has strong ties to Wallula. No doubt some of the early loggers traveled through Wallula Gap on their way between the forests of the Inland Northwest (the Blue Mountains, Idaho and the Okanogan Highlands) and the forests of the Cascades and Coast Ranges. Logs and wood chips go downriver on barges. Adjacent to a large pulp and paper mill is a farm of fast-growing cottonwoods.

The grain elevators in the Wallula area reveal the importance of the Columbia and Snake rivers for transportation of wheat. With locks on the eight dams between Lewiston, Idaho, and Portland, Oregon, tugs and barges are the least expensive way to ship wheat (and some other bulk materials) between the Inland Northwest and coastal harbors; most of the wheat is destined for Asia.

The Wallula area is at the center of energy production of the Pacific Northwest. High voltage wires on big towers go in all directions from the dams and other electricity generators; they stretch high above Juniper Canyon a few miles east of the Columbia River. Trains bring coal from the Great Plains to the thermal electric facility at Boardman in the Umatilla Basin. The Northwest's only operating nuclear power plant is at the Hanford Reservation in the Pasco Basin. Fuel barges are towed upriver through Wallula Gap

A tug pushes barges up the reservoir. Above the basalt cliffs and talus on the west side of Wallula Gap is a large vineyard. (Bob Carson photo)

Hundreds of wind turbines generate electricity on the Horse Heaven Hills east and west of Wallula Gap. (Bob Carson photo)

A lone sailboat near the Port Kelley grain elevators on the east shore of Lake Wallula. (Bob Baker photo)

The *Columbia Queen* on Lake Wallula. (Bob Baker photo)

to huge tanks at the mouth of Snake River. A natural gas pipeline running from Alberta, Canada, to California is buried just east of Wallula. Biofuels production is operating and planned for Wallula.

The abundant water in this desert is needed to cool thermal electric facilities, be they heated by the fission of uranium or the burning of fossil fuels. The nearby gas pipeline, the train tracks that extend to open-pit coal mines almost a thousand miles to the east, the potential cooling water, and a pro-industry attitude make this area irresistible for fossil fuel electric plants. What about air quality? On windy days Wallula has a lot of particulates in the atmosphere, in part due to tilling the soil for crops. On calm days the area is subject to temperature inversions, which trap pollutants from vehicles, woodstoves, industry, etc.

A large proportion of the wind turbines in the Northwest stretch along the crest of the Horse Heaven Hills. Within the past few years FPL Energy has erected almost 500 wind turbines just east of Wallula Gap. The towers of the Stateline wind farm, 165 feet high, have blades 77 feet long. Turning at only 28 revolutions per minute, these machines are quiet and relatively friendly to birds and bats. Some consider the wind farms an eyesore; others find them majestic for their engineering and architecture. A few believe their electricity is too expensive; most praise them for their generation of electricity with no fuel and no pollution. Other companies have larger wind turbines both east and west of the Stateline project.

Wallula, with a population of 227 (2000 census), is not generally recognized as a transportation hub. However, U.S. Highway 12 was widened to four lanes from Wallula northwest to Interstate 182 in the Tri-Cities, and widening Highway 12 east to Walla Walla began in 2008. U.S. Highway 730 goes from Wallula Junction southwest to the Umatilla Basin (see appendix 1: Road Log). Railroad tracks line both sides of the Columbia River through Wallula Gap; trains connecting Washington's Pasco Basin to Oregon's Willamette Valley carry vehicles, lumber and other goods. Perhaps the most significant way in which Wallula is a gateway to transportation is the tug and barge traffic along the reservoirs of the Columbia and Snake rivers: the barges carry wheat, wood chips, fuel, retired nuclear reactors, etc.

Gone are the days when a valley here became an avenue for a lava flow. No longer do floods laden with sediment and icebergs rush through the gateway. Canoes have been replaced with tugs and barges, sailboats, and fishing boats. Birds still catch or fight the southwesterly winds focused through Wallula Gap. The gateway is part of a flyway for migratory birds; many stop at McNary National Wildlife Refuge en route to the lakes of the Channeled Scabland to the north and Malheur National Wildlife Refuge to the south. Most important, Wallula is a gateway for the Columbia, the mightiest river in the Pacific Northwest, and for the salmon of the Columbia and its tributaries.

Bibliography

Mighetto, Lisa and W.J. Ebel, 1994, "Saving the salmon: A history of the U.S. Army Corps of Engineers efforts to protect anadromous fish on the Columbia and Snake rivers": Seattle, Historical Research Associates, 262 p.

Moulton, G.E., ed., 1988, *The definitive journals of Lewis & Clark through the Rockies to the Pacific*: Lincoln, Nebraska, University of Nebraska Press, v. 5, 415 p.

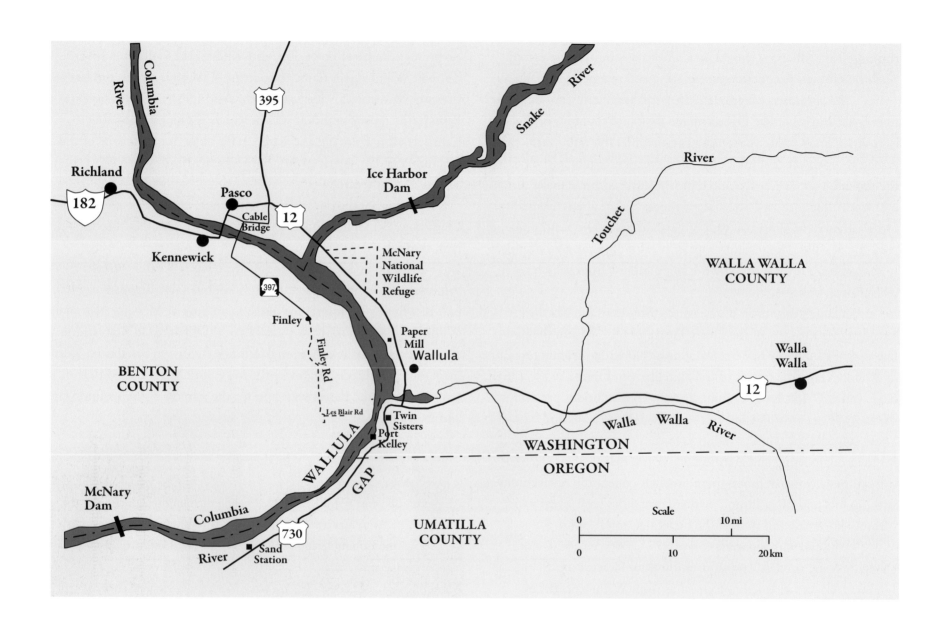

Appendix 1

Wallula Gap Road Log: Sand Station, Oregon, to Wallula Cemetery, Washington

Robert J. Carson and Michael E. Denny

Mileage

0.0   Sand Station Recreation Area (Army Corps of Engineers), about 9 miles southwest of the Washington-Oregon border on U.S. Highway 730. Toilets, camping, beach on Lake Wallula. Large rafts of waterfowl are on the Columbia River here during autumn and winter. In spring, watch for horned grebes, western grebes and ospreys. Plants include sand dock and wallflowers. Look for insect and rodent tracks in the sand. Go north on U.S. Highway 730.

0.1   Turnout on left.

0.2   Irrigation pumps on left.

0.3   Basalt outcrop on right.

0.5   The first tree along the shoreline is used by bald eagles in winter and ospreys in summer as a resting/hunting perch. Dragonflies are abundant here in summer.

0.6   Milepost 195. Turnout on left.

0.7   Dunes and trees along the shoreline. The black locusts and a few willows have Bullock's orioles and their hanging sock nests in summer. Spring brings desert butterflies into this area. During fall migration, watch for Neotropical birds in migration. Where are they headed?

0.9   Beach on Lake Wallula. Turnout on left. Look at the lone black cottonwood tree that is native to this area. Note where beavers have gnawed on the tree, which has survived several attempts by the animals to cut it down. It is frequently used as a perch by fish-eating osprey.

To the north across the Columbia River is the mouth of Spukshowski Canyon that begins as several narrow valleys beginning

Sand Station on Lake Wallula is a good place to picnic, camp and recreate year-round. (Dianne Kornberg photo)

nine miles to the north. The valleys, one named Switzer Canyon, have been cut into loess and basalt by intermittent streams. The valley heads just south of the crest of the Horse Heaven Hills anticlinal ridge. Near its mouth, Spukshowski Canyon is as much as 380 feet deep. About 30 American Indians once lived at this Umatilla summer fishing camp.

1.0   Irrigation pumps on left.

1.2   Turnout on left.

1.5   Irrigation pumps on left. Here is an island of antelope bush, also known as bitterbrush or buckbrush. This native plant is essential winter food for mule deer and many other herbivores. It is also vital to many native birds as a source of thermal cover in winter. Antelope bush blooms bright gold in April and is important to populations of spring insects.

1.6   Milepost 196.

2.0-2.1 The pond on the right is a great spot to see red-winged blackbirds and native amphibians in spring. In fall, ducks such as northern shovelers and green-winged teal use this pond. Also watch for muskrats and the occasional river otter.

2.4-2.7 Pond on right (milepost 197 at mileage 2.6). Watch for otters here as well. This pond is vital for salamanders and frogs to live and breed. The bulrushes scattered around the pond attract many dragonflies in spring and summer. Watch for loons out on the river from October through March.

2.9   Small pond on right. Look up to the right to see one of the few remaining active sand dunes in Wallula Gap. It is covered with different animal tracks and wind-formed ripples. In summer, watch for black-billed magpies and western kingbirds here.

3.2   Enter Wallula Gap at "ROCKS" sign. Basalt cliff on right. Here the lower lava flows are part of the Wanapum Basalt, and the higher lava flows are part of the Saddle Mountains Basalt. Scan the river for Caspian terns in summer and bald eagles in winter.

U.S. Highway 730 goes over the railroad tracks. In places

Antelope bush, also called bitterbrush or buckbrush. (Bob Carson photo)

there are what appear to be fences between the highway and the railroad tracks; these are railroad rockfall warning devices. Note that the mesh size of the "fence" is approximately the height of the rails above the ties. Little harm will come to a train if a small rock gets through the "fence"; if the rock is between the tracks, the train can pass over it. A large rock will hit against the "fence," resulting in a semaphore going red; the train will stop before it reaches the rockfall. The railroad rockfall warning devices will not prevent damage to a train that happens to pass at the instant of a large rock fall.

3.4   Turnout on right.

3.6   Milepost 198.

3.8   Turnout on right. Listen for these birds in Wallula Gap: canyon wrens with their sweet descending song echoing off the rocks and the introduced chukar with its loud *kerr-ruck*. Watch for swallows up high in summer and American white pelicans over the river anytime of year. The native bunchgrass growing on the steep slope is important food for deer, bighorn sheep, marmots and other rodents.

     To the north is the only named canyon on the northwest side of Wallula Gap; Spaw Canyon is less than two miles long.

4.1   Turnout on right. Below the cliffs is a slope covered with grasses, wildflowers and sagebrush. The 35-degree slope is a talus of rocks that have fallen from the cliffs above. The cut at the base of the talus reveals white Mazama ash from the eruption of Crater Lake 7,700 years ago.

4.5   Turnout for Juniper Canyon Unit of McNary National Wildlife Refuge on right. This is the place to park for the most extensive hiking in Wallula Gap. The bedrock is all Columbia River basalt; outcrops by the creek are Wanapum Basalt, whereas the "scabs" at the top of the canyon are younger Saddle Mountains basalt. Two crude trails lead eastward along the sides of Juniper Canyon; both become faint in about a mile. However, this country is open, and game and cattle trails abound.

     The trail on the south side of Juniper Canyon starts at the gate and climbs up and over several sandy benches. Within a few minutes of walking, there are two large juniper trees to the north and a patch of bare sand high to the south. Note the fragile

The mouth of Juniper Canyon from the west: On the floor is the wetland created by back-flooding behind McNary Dam. To the left are basalt cliffs. To the right are sandy benches of unknown geologic origin. A half mile up the canyon is the proposed dam site. Juniper Canyon is a unit of McNary National Wildlife Refuge. (Bob Carson photo)

Lower Juniper Canyon: Note beaver ponds behind the juniper tree. (Bob Carson photo)

Upper Juniper Canyon: Note the difference in vegetation density between the north-facing, shady slope on the right; the bottom along the tiny creek; and the south-facing, sunny slope on the left. (Bob Carson photo)

How many hundreds of years old is this western juniper? (Dianne Kornberg photo)

Sand dune on the south face of Juniper Canyon: The sand was blown here from the Umatilla Basin by the prevailing southwesterly winds. (Bob Carson photo)

Above: This gneiss erratic boulder transported on an iceberg by the Missoula floods rests at the top of Juniper Canyon 600 feet above Lake Wallula. (Bob Carson photo)
Left: Granitic erratic boulder far from home.
(Dianne Kornberg photo)

biological soil crusts (cryptobiotic soil crusts) on either side of the trail. At an elevation of 760 feet, small juniper trees grow on sand that overlies a giant gravel bar deposited by the Missoula floods. At the outside of a right turn, Juniper "Creek" has undercut the eddy bar to expose the thick, steeply dipping gravels. Along the creek 400 feet below are beaver ponds and wetland vegetation. Farther east are dune complexes with patches of bare sand. The winds named the Prevailing Westerlies have blown the sand here from the Umatilla Basin. Juniper Canyon is a sand trap; the creek in the bottom prevents the sand from being transported farther northeast.

The trail along the north side of Juniper Canyon stays close to the wetland and passes by beaver dams. The scabland topography high above is due to erosion by the Missoula floods; one example is the erosion remnant noted on the topographic map as having an elevation of 975 feet. On the south side of the 975-foot hill, and farther east up to an elevation of 1,030 feet, are granitic boulders up to 6 feet in diameter. These erratic boulders were deposited here during the melting of icebergs stranded at the "shorelines" of the Missoula floods. To the northeast, above the level of the Missoula floods, loess covers the basalt.

4.6   Bridge over Juniper "Creek"; milepost 199.

5.6   Milepost 200. Watch and listen for your first prairie falcon here. These big, native falcons live along these basalt rims, protect their territories, and hunt pigeons and rodents. This is a good spot to see mule deer as well.

6.0   Turnout on right.

6.6   Rock outcrop on left; milepost 201.

7.1   Turnout on right. Look up along the tops of the rocks for yellow-bellied marmots in spring and early summer; these big rodents go below ground after the hot weather sets in and drop into a sleep called aestivation. Up in the basalt rims above are several areas where bats roost and fly out during warm spring and summer evenings. Watch the river for western grebes and northern gulls in winter.

7.2   "ROCKS" sign. The lava flows here are Wanapum Basalt at road level and Saddle Mountains Basalt at the top of the canyon.

7.6   Milepost 202.

7.9   Turnout on right. This is a good place for an "up close and personal" look at Columbia River basalt. The lava flows at road level are the Frenchman Springs Member of the Wanapum Basalt and are, therefore, about 15.3 million years old. At that time this area was perhaps at about the same elevation but without cliffs or river. The lava flows, more like lava lakes than lava rivers, came from the east. Low in the basalt at road level are longer, more regular columns (called a *colonnade*); higher there are smaller columns (called an *entablature*). At the top is flow top breccia, caused by the surface cooling and solidifying, then being broken as the still-molten interior continued to move. In the flow top breccia, one can see ropey texture, or *pahoehoe*, the actual crust of the lava flow that folded and chilled. The dark basalt is mostly tiny crystals of the minerals *plagioclase* and *pyroxene*, with lots of volcanic glass. There are also *phenocrysts* (large crystals of plagioclase) and *vesicles* (volcanic gas bubble cavities). Some of the vesicles are filled with minerals deposited during and after cooling of the lava flow; these filled vesicles or *amygdules* may contain silica (quartz or opal), *zeolites* (a family of minerals that you may have heard about in connection with water softeners), or calcium carbonate (*calcite*). The top of a lava flow may be reddish due to oxidation before or during the emplacement of the overlying basalt.

8.0-8.1 In the pond on the right look for Virginia rail and muskrats during the warm season.

8.3   Basalt outcrop on left.

8.6   Milepost 203.

8.8   Oregon-Washington state line. Turnout on right. There's a lot of biology and geology to be seen here, but look out for rattlesnakes. In spring and summer watch the sky above the basalt rims for white-throated swifts; these birds have very rapid wing beats, and their *cheee-cheee* calls bounce off the rock walls. In spring many wildflowers bloom here.

From the turnout, walk southwesterly along the road to a large gully, or southerly across the alluvial fan to the mouth of the canyon. If it is raining, an intermittent stream may be flowing out of the canyon and percolating into the floor of the gully. During rare heavy rains, water coming down the canyon may be mixed with mud (derived from the loess above) and rocks (broken loose from the bedrock). The combination, called a *debris flow*, surges out across the surface of the alluvial fan, depositing the mud and rocks. When this last happened here, about 1970, the debris flow went over the highway, blocked traffic, and endangered trains. After the mess was cleaned up, the gully was enlarged in hopes of containing the next debris flow.

The canyon is, of course, erosional, having been cut by running water. A semi-circular or triangular, gently sloping landform called an *alluvial fan* extends from the mouth of the canyon to the highway. The fan is composed of both *alluvium* (stream sediment) and debris flow deposits. Sediment transported down the canyon is deposited when the water spreads out on the fan. Near the top of the fan are large boulders deposited during the last debris flow. In the gully sides, you can see a poorly sorted mixture of mud and angular cobbles from earlier precipitation events.

Also notice the powdery, light-colored, fine-grained deposit. If it were white it would be pure Mazama ash from the eruption that formed Crater Lake 7,700 years ago. But the ash is mixed with reworked tan loess to give the mixture an off-white color. This ash was not directly deposited here, meaning it did not fall from the sky and accumulate to this great thickness. When ancient Mount Mazama erupted 7,700 years ago, the ash drifted to the north and east, settling out to a thickness of about an inch on the Horse Heaven Hills. Rain then washed the ash and the loess off the hillsides and into the canyon; the stream deposited the dirty ash here. Look across the river at two, much-larger alluvial fans; in the railroad cuts you can see thick layers of light-colored Mazama ash.

To the northeast and southwest of the canyon rise basalt cliffs. Below the cliffs lie huge *taluses*, or sloping heaps of angular rock fragments. The basalt flows have lots of joints, mostly from cooling and contraction millions of years ago. Weathering, for example by water freezing in a joint, loosens rocks, which fall to build a talus. Taluses have slopes of 35 degrees, the "angle of repose" for angular rocks.

9.4   Large turnout on right. See the interpretive sign about the Lewis and Clark expedition, which camped nearby on October 18, 1805. In daylight from March through June, listen to the sounds of this desert. The place is alive with animals in the evening and early in the morning. In particular, listen for the song of the canyon wren.

9.8   Milepost 1. In 1805, Lewis and Clark noted an American Indian village somewhere to the northwest, now beneath the reservoir.

10.1   Private road on right leads up Spring Gulch, one of the largest valleys tributary to Wallula Gap. It is named for a few, small springs issuing from basalts exposed on the valley floor and in side canyons. Water flows rarely in the intermittent stream along the valley axis. If it is a sunny morning, stop to listen for lazuli buntings singing in the golden currants over against the talus slope. In spring watch for common ravens and white-throated swifts. In fall and winter scan the river for loons.

At the mouth of Spring Gulch, north of the private road, is a small borrow pit. The bottom of this excavation reveals 6 feet of volcanic ash from Mount Mazama. After the volcano exploded and collapsed to form Crater Lake 7,700 years ago, rain washed the ash off the hillsides above. The ash was deposited along the former

channel of the intermittent stream in Spring Gulch. Today the lens of ash is exposed in the borrow pit; the intermittent stream has a new channel just to the north.

Much of the valley floor is comprised of sediment: alluvium along the channel and in small alluvial fans at the mouths of side canyons; redeposited loess and Mazama ash; and an eddy bar deposited by the Missoula floods. As these floods rushed through Wallula Gap like shotgun blasts, the water that went up tributary canyons slowed in the eddies, resulting in eddy bars of gravel, with tops well above the floor of Wallula Gap (300 feet), but well below the maximum elevation of the floods (1,250 feet). The eddy

"The Rock Ranch" in Spring Gulch lies on the edge of a gravel bar deposited by the Missoula floods. (Bob Carson photo)

bar along Spring Gulch has been somewhat eroded since the last Missoula flood, but the western edge of what remains is at 680 feet. The eddy bar, with a top that rises gently to the east, extends more than half a mile along Spring Gulch. The intermittent stream has cut through the upper sediments in the eddy bar. The largest clasts are angular basalt, with boulders as much as 4 feet in diameter ripped from nearby sources by the high-velocity floods. Rounded cobbles, with many exotic lithologies like granite and quartzite, were carried from great distances by these floods. One angular boulder of gneiss was likely carried to the eddy bar by an iceberg. Within the gravels are lenses of bedded sand deposited as the currents slowed; the strata

White, powdery Mazama ash from the eruption of Crater Lake 7,700 years ago is exposed in a borrow pit at the mouth of Spring Gulch. (Bob Carson photo)

generally dip gently westward. In places there are thin beds of silt at irregular intervals; each probably records the end of a flood.

On the west side of Wallula Gap are two much-larger eddy bars. Their flat tops, which slope gently eastward, have elevations above 800 feet. Both are visible from here, one due west, and the largest to the northwest. Each has huge gullies that lead to large alluvial fans behind the railroad tracks.

10.8   Milepost 2.

10.9   Northwest Grain Growers road on left to Port Kelley.

11.1   Grain elevators on left.

11.4   Yacht club on left.

11.5   "ROCKS" sign. Turnout on left. In the spring this is a good area to look at wildflowers and native grasses.

11.6   In the roadcut is white Mazama ash from the Crater Lake eruption 7,700 years ago.

11.8   Milepost 3. In the evening this is a good spot to see river otters or even a mink along the river. Also watch for mule deer on the hillsides.

12.0   Here is the hunting territory of a peregrine falcon. Maybe you will be lucky enough to see this fast-flying bird of prey.

12.5   Abandoned county road to right.

12.6-12.7   Highway goes through dune field. These are parabolic dunes, which are convex in a downwind direction and have horns pointing upwind (southwest). The sand supply for the mostly vegetated dunes was sandbars along the Columbia River; the sandbars were drowned by Lake Wallula.

12.8   Milepost 4.

12.9   Twin Sisters (Two Sisters) turnout on right. In 1818 fur trader Alexander Ross noted these "two singular towering rocks similar in colour, shape and height." According to an American Indian legend, coyote turned two sisters into these basalt towers. This is Wallula Gap National Natural Landmark, an excellent place for a short hike or a picnic; the view from between the towers is breathtaking. Climb over or under the fence, and follow the trail eastward to a minor saddle just south of the Twin Sisters. From here you can climb north to between the two pillars, walk east to the nearby dunes, or hike south a short way onto a plateau. As of March 2001, it is illegal to rock climb on the Twin Sisters. Also, be careful not to trespass on the 40 acres of private land behind the fence just east of the dunes.

There are many Columbia River basalt flows exposed here, mostly of the Frenchman Springs Member of the Wanapum Basalt. Let's concentrate on the "Two Sisters flow," which is about 15.3 million years old, similar to the rest of the Frenchman Springs lava flows. Notice that the columns in the base of the Twin Sisters are much larger than those within the towers themselves. The base is

The railroad and U.S. Highway 730 wind along the east shore of Lake Wallula from the Twin Sisters to the yacht club and grain elevators at Port Kelley. (Bob Carson photo)

Behind the light-colored sand is a miniature Channeled Scabland of basalt cliffs. Compare this image with one taken about a hundred years earlier (see Introduction, page 2). Little has changed except the vegetation. (Dianne Kornberg photo)

called a *colonnade*; the larger columns result from slower cooling at the base of the flow, with the heat presumably going down into the preexisting rocks below. The smaller columns of the Twin Sisters themselves (the *entablature* of the "Two Sisters flow") are due to faster cooling, the heat going up into the air. Water would have further increased the cooling rate and resulted in smaller, less-regular columns. The climate here in the Miocene, when these flows were erupted, was moist and subtropical; there was a lot of rain. Another possibility for water is ponded drainage: The lava flows disrupted the existing drainage system creating local lakes.

Why are there so many cliffs in this area? The term "Channeled Scabland" was given to the area of eastern Washington crossed by the Missoula floods. The floods released during repeated failures of the ice dam that blocked glacial Lake Missoula cut huge channels, like Grand Coulee, Moses Coulee and, nearer to here, Devils Canyon and others in the vicinity of Palouse Falls. Scabs like Steamboat Rock in upper Grand Coulee are erosion remnants, portions of lava flows that survived the severe erosion by the floods. In this miniature "Channeled Scabland," there is a network of flood channels. The floods came from the north and locally the northwest, and the water rushed to the southwest and locally the west. And there are scabs or erosion remnants in all directions: to the west the small *buttes* (higher than wide) of the Twin Sisters; to the north larger *mesas* (wider than high) as high as 783 feet (elevation); to the southeast a conical erosion remnant with a top at 1,120 feet. The floor of the river (bottom of Lake Wallula) is at about 300 feet elevation, so the Missoula floods had to be deeper than 800 feet to scour that conical erosion remnant! Evidence elsewhere indicates that the floods' maximum elevation was more than 1,200 feet. The dunes

here are at an elevation of about 500 feet; imagine 700 feet of water above you.

Notice that the rocks are dark but that the sand is very light. The sand includes light-colored grains of quartz, feldspar rich in sodium and potassium, and some muscovite, minerals not present in basalt. The light-colored minerals are abundant in granite, which is found "upstream" in the North Cascades, the Okanogan Highlands, southeastern British Columbia, central Idaho, and northeastern Oregon, places containing the headwaters of the Columbia and Snake rivers and their tributaries. Granitic and other rocks are weathered and eroded there; the sediment gets into the *fluvial* (river) system and is transported to Wallula Gap and elsewhere. Some of the sediment gets deposited in bars adjacent to the river. When the water level drops, the wind erodes sand from the bars, transports it downwind and deposits dunes. As the dominant winds are the Prevailing Westerlies, most of the transport is to the northeast. Look southwest for a source for this dune sand. None is visible because the Lake Wallula reservoir inundated the sandbars in 1953. Therefore, these dunes are starved of sand and slowly become more vegetated.

Faint subhorizontal, subparallel steps bedeck the slopes at the bases of the cliffs. One name for these steps is *terracettes*, or little terraces. These terracettes are in *colluvium*, earth materials slowly creeping downslope. Here the colluvium is a mixture of silt and angular rocks. Each terracette has two parts: a more or less level top or tread, which may have less vegetation than the rest of the slope; and a slanted riser with abundant grasses and other vegetation. The terracettes are a few feet apart up and down the slope. The origin of terracettes is controversial. Some scientists believe they are geologic: old shorelines, or small slumps. Terracettes are widespread in eastern

The Twin Sisters with dune sand behind. Note the three prominent fractures in the two towers; such fractures helped the Missoula floods erode the basalt flows. (Bob Carson photo)

Washington and Oregon, as well as the Appalachians, the Alps, Peru and New Zealand. They occur on a wide variety of rocks and sediments and usually have about the same size and spacing. It seems that if they were geologic in origin, the terracettes would have different dimensions on different types of rocks and sediments, but that, if made by grazing animals, the terracettes would have similar dimensions. Some scientists propose combination theories of origin, with geologic features being modified by animal tracks, or animal paths initiating slope failures. What do you think? Incidentally, cattle were excluded from this area in the 1970s.

13.0, 13.4   Basalt outcrops on left.

What made these little terraces? Was it mass wasting (e.g., soil creep)? Was it animals (e.g., cattle and deer)? Was it both?
Left: Mogul-like terracettes. **Right:** Step-like terracettes. (Bob Carson photos)

13.5   Boulders in fracture on right. **(Park at the turnout 0.1 mile north to see this feature. Look up as you walk along the highway, being very careful of traffic.)** The many narrow, closely spaced cracks formed in a polygonal pattern as the lava cooled and shrank. In this vicinity the lower columns (the *colonnade*) of each lava flow have cracks about 3 feet apart (columns about 3 feet in diameter); the upper columns (the *entablature*) of these lava flows have cracks about 1 foot apart (columns about 1 foot in diameter).

Notice that there are large wide cracks spaced tens of feet apart. These are fractures due to tectonism, slight bending and tilting of the rocks of the Columbia Plateau. These fractures were initially narrow but have been widened by weathering and other "normal" geologic processes. The Missoula floods took advantage of these weak places to widen the fractures even more.

One of the cracks has three or four boulders ("chock stones") wedged near the top, more than 100 feet above you. Their diameters of 2 feet to 4 feet suggest that they are derived from a colonnade. The sizes of the adjacent columns (mostly 1 feet to 2 feet) indicate that the chock stones are wedged in an entablature.

There are at least two possibilities as to how these boulders got wedged in the fracture. One is that they fell down from a colonnade above. However, above the crack is a wide bench on top of the entablature. (It is easy to walk up there from the turnout [mile 13.6]; be careful of rattlesnakes. There is a great view down the fracture to the chock stones.) Furthermore, one would expect the boulders to be angular if they had fallen from above.

The other possibility is that the chock stones were transported (plucked, then rolled) here by one or more Missoula floods. If so, the transport distance is not far, for the boulders are not

well-rounded. What do you think?

13.6   Turnout on right. **Use this turnout to walk south to see boulders in crack (mile 13.5) or north to see pillow basalt (mile 13.9). Be careful of traffic.**

13.8   Milepost 5.

13.9   Pillow basalt on right. Most of the basalt in the large cliff has columnar joints because of eruptions on land. However, just above road level is a small exposure of pillow basalt in one of the flows of the Frenchman Springs Member of the Wanapum Basalt. Here basalt flowed into water and formed the rounded masses with dark interiors and orange borders. Oxidation of dark, iron-bearing silicate minerals results in rust-colored iron oxides and hydroxides.

14.1   Cross Olympic-Wallowa lineament. Small turnout on left. **Be careful of traffic if you are going to cross the road in your vehicle or on foot.** In the rock outcrop just southwest of the turnout are half a dozen narrow, near-vertical places where the basalt is broken and discolored. Each of these places is a small fault that is part of the Wallula fault zone, part of the much longer Olympic-Wallowa lineament (OWL). As originally proposed by cartographer Erwin Raisz in 1945, the OWL extended from the Strait of Juan de Fuca southeasterly all the way across Washington to the north side of Oregon's Wallowa Mountains. The OWL is a much-debated major feature. From Cle Elum, Washington, southeast to beyond Milton-Freewater, Oregon, the OWL is coincident with a young fault. It offsets deposits of Glacial Lake Missoula floods on the Hanford

Chock stones in cracks in basalt cliffs.
Top Left: Chock stones in two cracks on the right show up in this snowy, winter scene. (Mike Denny photo)
Bottom Left: Chock stone with Lake Wallula below. (Bob Carson photo)
Above: How did this chock stone get in this crack? Did it fall from above, or was it deposited by a Missoula flood? Note pigeon under chock stone for scale. (Bob Carson photo)

Site; movement along the Wallula fault zone probably caused the magnitude 6 Stateline earthquake (in the Walla Walla Valley near Milton-Freewater) on July 15, 1936.

At each of these small faults the originally black basalt is yellowish from oxidation facilitated because movement along the faults broke the basalt; increased surface area enhanced chemical weathering. In places there is coarse *fault breccia*, basalt crushed to fist-sized chunks. Elsewhere fault movement has ground the basalt to very fine-grained *fault gouge* – soft, yellowish, clay-like material.

What is the direction of movement along the Wallula fault zone, which here separates the Pasco Basin to the north and the Horse Heaven Hills to the south? Since the top of the basalts is below sea level in the center of the Pasco Basin, the Horse Heaven Hills are structurally higher, that is, on the upthrown side of the fault zone. (Some of this structural relief is due to the upfolding of the Horse Heaven Hills anticline.) Locally, then, the Wallula fault zone is a near vertical *dip-slip* (vertical motion) fault with the south side up relative to the north side. To the east of here, triangular *faceted spurs* mark the north ends of small ridges truncated by the fault zone. Faceted spurs indicate dip-slip motion, with the north side down. However, at the westernmost of the half dozen small faults in this road cut, there are faint *slickenlines*, scratches on the rocks showing the direction of fault movement. These subhorizontal slickenlines indicate *strike-slip* (sideways) motion. In summary, it appears that over time the Wallula fault zone in this area has experienced both dip-slip and strike-slip movement.

Northeast of the turnout is the delta of the Walla Walla River. When McNary Dam was completed in 1953, an arm of Lake Wallula drowned the lower few miles of the meandering Walla Walla

Fault in basalt just west of Wallula Junction. This fault, the westernmost of a group of parallel faults in this basalt cliff along the Olympic-Wallowa lineament, is marked by coarse-grained breccia (broken rocks), fine-grained gouge, accelerated weathering (yellowish iron oxides and hydroxides), and subhorizontal slickenlines. (Bob Carson photos)

River. This arm of the reservoir filled with sediment within a few years; the delta of the Walla Walla River has been deposited in Lake Wallula since then. The oldest part of the delta is tree covered; the youngest westernmost part is a marsh.

Lewis and Clark camped at the mouth of the Walla Walla River in April 1806. The explorers described the river as "a handsome stream about 4½ feet deep and 50 yards wide." On the topographic map of 1918 (based on a 1915 survey), the Walla Walla River is shown to join the Columbia River about one mile west of here.

14.3   Road to Port of Wallula on left. **If you are careful of trains**, this is a good place to look at geology in railroad cuts. A flow of the Saddle Mountains Basalt and Touchet Beds deposited by the Missoula floods are exposed here. Park just across the tracks, and then walk east. It is safer to walk along the tops of the railroad cuts (**watching for rattlesnakes**) than along the tracks. **Do not cross the railroad bridge over the Walla Walla River.**

The first railroad cut is through a basalt flow of the Umatilla Member of the Saddle Mountains Basalt. The basalt here, about 14 million years old, exhibits spheroidal weathering. The columnar joints in the flow are about 1 to 3 feet apart. Weathering has proceeded into the columns from the joints, where water can penetrate. Corners have more surface area than the sides of the columns, so weathering is concentrated at corners. As the outsides of the originally angular columns decay, the remaining interiors become more rounded, resulting ultimately in rounded dark corestones (not yet decayed) surrounded by rust-colored weathered material. Chemical weathering of iron silicates in the basalt produces these "rusty" iron oxides and hydroxides. Here, the corestones range from less than an inch to more than a foot in diameter.

There are two more railroad cuts (separated by a small northwest-trending draw) to the northeast of the basalt. In these two cuts, clastic dikes cut Touchet Beds. Notice that the dozen or so subhorizontal Touchet Beds exhibit rhythmic or cyclic bedding, with each bed half a foot to a foot thick. Typical Touchet Beds grade from coarser sediment (sand or even gravel) at the base to finer sediment (silt) at the top, indicating slowing current. Here the range in grain size is not much. Each of the beds has undulating laminae (thin layers deposited by water currents that made ripple marks on the sediment surface). The consensus of most geologists is that each bed represents a separate flood from Glacial Lake Missoula, with the ice dam failing at intervals of a few decades to a few years. However, the alternative minority opinion claims that these beds represent only one catastrophic flood, with each bed representing a separate surge of

Missoula flood and eolian sediments in railroad cut. Several Touchet Beds (slackwater sands and silts deposited by the Missoula floods) are overlain by a few feet of loess (silt deposited by the wind). (Bob Carson photo)

floodwaters. Separate surges could result from a piecemeal failure of the ice dam and/or the floodwaters taking different routes from western Montana to Wallula.

Above the Touchet Beds lie 3 feet of loess (windblown silt) deposited since the last Missoula flood. Notice that, unlike the underlying bedded and laminated Touchet Beds, the loess is massive, with crude columnar joints due to shrinkage after the silt settled out of suspension.

Clastic dikes are particularly prominent in the last (or northeastern) railroad cut before the bridge over the Walla Walla River. The term *dike* usually refers to a tabular, cross-cutting igneous feature, a place where magma was being injected along a fissure. However, these clastic dikes resulted from injection of water-saturated sediment through the Touchet Beds. The subvertical dikes range from less than an inch to half a foot thick. The larger dikes have alternating bands of sand and silt. There have been dozens of papers written on the clastic dikes in the Touchet Beds. How did the cracks that hold the dikes form? Theories range from desiccation and/or low-temperature contraction to loading (by floodwaters from Glacial Lake Missoula) and landslides. Were the sediments in the dikes injected downward, upward, once, many times? Kevin Pogue, geologist at Whitman College, uses data, including the presence of clastic dikes injected downward into basalt bedrock, to support an earthquake hypothesis. The proximity of the Olympic-Wallowa lineament to the clastic dikes in the Touchet Beds supports this theory.

Beyond the second railroad cut in the Touchet Beds lies the bridge over the Walla Walla River. Rather than cross the potentially dangerous railroad bridge, stop before it for a view of the lowermost

Walla Walla River and its delta. Before the construction of McNary Dam, this river meandered three miles from here to its confluence with the Columbia River. The channel across the floodplain was lined with sand and gravel bars. In 1953 the lower Walla Walla River was backflooded by Lake Wallula, but the river has rapidly extended its delta out into the reservoir. Looking northwest beyond the river's mouth you can see driftwood stumps and logs that indicate shallow water far beyond the vegetated part of the delta. The fine-grained deltaic sediments stretch far across Lake Wallula. Someday dredging will be required to maintain a shipping channel along the Columbia River.

14.7   Turn left before the weigh station. In spring the hills to your right are covered with what look like beautiful purple bouquets;

Old postcard of former Oregon-Washington Railroad & Navigation Company railroad bridge over the Walla Walla River at Wallula. (Fred L. Mitchell Collection)

these are clumps of phlox.

14.8   Milepost 6.

14.9   Stop at highway junction. Turn left toward the Tri-Cities.

15.0   Bridge over the Walla Walla River. The old highway bridge is to the right. The railroad bridge and the delta are to the left. The trees and mudflats of the Walla Walla River delta are a natural history treasure; birds by the thousands depend on this area year-round. Early naturalists Thomas Nuttall, John Townsend and Charles Bendire collected here for the Smithsonian Institution. Lewis and Clark camped down the "Wallahwallah River" on April 29, 1806.

15.2   Approximate location of the old Wallula townsite. Fort Nez Perce was located on the east shore of the Columbia River just above the mouth of the Walla Walla River. In 1818 the North West Company established a trading post at Fort Nez Perce. The Hudson's Bay Company acquired the North West Company in 1821, and Fort Nez Perce gradually became known as Fort Walla Walla. The fort was destroyed by fire in 1841 and rebuilt of adobe. Wallula, an important river port, was established in 1860 and platted in 1862. A second Wallula, platted in 1883 and sometimes called Wallula Junction, was an important railroad site. The current town of Wallula was platted in about 1953 in connection with the construction of McNary Dam and filling of the reservoir.

Fishermen on the old highway bridge over the Walla Walla River. (Dianne Kornberg photo)

New and old highway bridges across the mouth of the Walla Walla River. The Olympic-Wallowa lineament runs west-northwest along the base of the hill across Lake Wallula. (Bob Baker photo)

15.3   North Shore Road on right. If you turn here, you come to an immediate "Y" with a sign announcing that this is the Wallula Unit of McNary National Wildlife Refuge.

If you turn right again at this sign, in 0.2 mile you come to Madame Dorion Park on the right. Madame Dorion was an American Indian who traveled from Missouri to Wallula in 1811-12 with the Wilson Price Hunt Party of the Pacific Fur Company. At the west end of the park are toilets and camping. Picnic tables and a boat launch on the Walla Walla River are located 0.1 mile to the east. Roadcuts within the park expose Touchet Beds (slackwater sediments from Glacial Lake Missoula floods).

If, on the other hand, you turn left at the sign (Wallula Unit of McNary National Wildlife Refuge), soon you are driving on top of the Touchet Beds. In 0.4 mile there is a parking lot with a gazebo

In this David Manuel painting, an American Indian couple paddles a dugout canoe across the Columbia River from Fort Nez Perce. In the background are a native village at the mouth of the Walla Walla River and the north end of Wallula Gap, including the Twin Sisters. (Fred L. Mitchell Collection with permission from the Manuel family, Hot Lake Springs, LaGrande, Oregon)

overlooking a large pond on the Walla Walla River. The pond is the largest remaining portion of the arm of the reservoir that extended up the lower Walla Walla River when McNary Dam was built across the Columbia River. In the gazebo are interpretive signs about the waterfowl and other wildlife of this important wetland.

This pond is a shelter for many thousands of migratory birds during bad weather such as high winds out of Wallula Gap, sudden snow storms and rapidly advancing cold fronts. The onset of waterfowl hunting season also brings ducks and geese to this true refuge. Many wildlife species depend on this pond for survival during winter. Before this pond freezes over, the waterfowl attract bald eagles and other predators. In the spring, wall flowers, phlox, locoweeds and other plants all burst into bloom. The trees around this refuge pond are river birch, Russian olive, willow, cottonwood

and black locust. Mule and white-tailed deer, coyotes, beaver and even a few elk live in the nearby riparian areas. In the pond are Pacific chorus frogs, tiger salamanders and the ever-invasive American bullfrog. On warm spring evenings after a rain the spadefoot toads dig out of the sand and go into the night to find mates and lay eggs. The desert area around this pond is an island of the past. The native animals and plants here are surrounded by orchards, roads and railroads.

Behind the pond is quite a panorama from the Blue Mountains to Wallula Gap. Looking east one can see the top of the Blue Mountains far up the Walla Walla Valley. From southeast to

View southwest of the lower Walla Walla River and Wallula Gap. The little river meanders between ponds and then deposits its delta in the reservoir. The Columbia River slowly flows from Washington's Pasco Basin (foreground) through the Horse Heaven Hills to Oregon's Umatilla Basin (background). (Bob Carson photo)

Behind the lower Walla Walla River pond, wind turbines crown the Horse Heaven Hills east of Wallula Gap. (Bob Carson photo)

south is the FPL Energy wind farm atop the Horse Heaven Hills, with the Olympic-Wallowa lineament at the base of the ridge. Behind the grain elevators to the southwest is Wallula Gap, including the 8.5 million-year-old Ice Harbor lava flow remnant, which is the highest point on the northwest cliffs of the water gap.

15.4   Touchet Beds in roadcut on right. The Missoula floods deposited the Touchet Beds about 15,300 to 12,700 years ago (see mile 14.3 for further explanation).

15.7   Railroad overpass. On the bluff just to the west will be an interpretative site explaining the importance of Wallula Gap in terms of geology, biology and history. The access will be from the east side of the highway.

16.0   Private road on right.

16.5   Turn right on Columbia Way to Wallula. Lake Wallula is about two miles wide here. The former free-flowing Columbia River was near the west shore of the present reservoir.

16.6   Turn right at First Street in Wallula. (This is but one route through Wallula to the cemetery.)

16.7   Turn left on Ross Way.

16.8   Turn right on Second Street.

16.9   Cross Burdett Way.

17.0   Wallula Cemetery. A summary of the history of Wallula can be found at: http://www.interment.net/data/us/wa/wallawalla/wallula/wallula.htm. This website also includes a list of all the graves in this cemetery. The last burial in an older cemetery was in 1934. Many graves were moved to this new cemetery before the reservoir inundated them.

Despite nearby trees blocking part of the view, this is a good place to review the geography and geology of the area. Wallula lies in the Pasco Basin, where the basalt flows are buried by hundreds of feet of young sediment. The Horse Heaven Hills on the skyline rise behind the Olympic-Wallowa lineament, which stretches from

Cemetery at Wallula, with Wallula Gap in the distance. (Kathryn Farrell photo)

the northwest past Wallula Gap and on toward the southeast. Visible beneath the windmills east of Wallula Gap are a half dozen faceted spurs along the Wallula fault zone that makes up this part of the Olympic-Wallowa lineament. The Horse Heaven Hills are an anticline of basalt flows that are well-exposed in the cliffs at Wallula Gap (southwest). The Clearwater-Salmon River, later joined by the Columbia River and then the Snake River, first cut this water gap. Enormous floods from Glacial Lake Missoula caused severe erosion at Wallula Gap. This narrow gap acted as a hydraulic dam for these floods, slowing the water so that lots of sediment was deposited in the Pasco Basin and nearby valleys. The construction of McNary Dam after World War II formed modern Lake Wallula, inundating Wallula Gap and forcing the town of Wallula to higher ground.

Bibliography

Babcock, Scott and Bob Carson, 2000, *Hiking Washington's geology*: Seattle, The Mountaineers, 272 p.

Bjornstad, Bruce, 2006, *On the trail of the Ice Age floods: A geological field guide to the Mid-Columbia Basin*: Sandpoint, Idaho, Keokee Books, 308 p.

Carson, R.J. and K.R. Pogue, 1996, *Flood basalts and glacier floods: Roadside geology of parts of Walla Walla, Franklin, and Columbia Counties, Washington*: Washington Division of Geology and Earth Resources Information Circular 90, 47 p.

Majors, H.M., 1975, *Exploring Washington*: Holland, Michigan, Van Winkle Publishing Co., 177 p.

Appendix 2

Wallula Gap Road Log: Kennewick, Washington, to High Point on West Side of Wallula Gap

Robert J. Carson

Mileage

0.0   South end of cable bridge over Columbia River in Kennewick, Washington; go south on Washington Route 397 through the eastern part of Kennewick; follow Route 397 (Chemical Road) to Finley.

5.7   Turn right (south), cross railroad tracks, and drive through Finley on Finley Road. With the exception of a few curves, this road goes due south across the Horse Heaven Hills to its end. Windmills are visible to the west.

8.3   Basalt quarry to east (left) as Finley Road goes up Nine Canyon and an unnamed draw. You have just crossed the Olympic-Wallowa lineament, which here is a fault. In the quarry, a fault and/

View across the Columbia River from the west side of Wallula Cap. (Bob Carson photo)

or clastic dikes related to earthquakes and/or the Missoula floods are exposed. (See chapter 3, "Geology," especially pages 56-57 and 70-71.)

9.1   Finley Road bends south. To the north is a gravel road leading to a communications tower on the summit of The Butte, elevation 1,140 feet. Just east of the summit is a group of granitic boulders deposited by an iceberg riding the Missoula floods. Walk to the summit to see these huge boulders and get an excellent view of the Pasco Basin.

10.7   Paved road becomes gravel road. On top of the Horse Heaven Hills, little bedrock is visible because the basalt is blanketed with at least 10 feet of loess (wind-deposited silt).

14.2   Crest of Horse Heaven Hills.

15.2   Junction with Meals Yellepit Road, which goes northeast. (This is a slightly longer route to return to Finley and Route 397.)

16.0   Junction with private road. Continue south on Finley Road, which turns east (left) for half a mile, crossing a draw.

16.9   Junction with Les Blair Road after Finley Road has turned south. Elevation 1,348 feet. Drive east on Les Blair Road (or if the road is closed, park here and walk east) one mile to an abandoned farm at top of Wallula Gap. Below are Palmer Pond, the Burlington Northern Railroad tracks, and Lake Wallula. Directly across the river is the Washington-Oregon state line. To the northeast are the grain elevators at Port Kelley.

Appendix 3

Fauna and Flora at Wallula
Gap with emphasis on native
mammals, reptiles, amphibians
and birds

   Michael E. Denny

MAMMALS

Wild Dogs
   Coyote
   Red fox (rare)
Wildcats
   Mountain lion (rare)
   Bobcat
Bats
   Little brown myotis
   Fringed myotis
   California myotis
   Small-footed myotis
   Yuma myotis
   Long-eared myotis
   Hoary bat
   Silvery-haired bat
   Big brown bat
   Western pipistrelle
   Spotted bat
   Pallid bat

Raccoons
   Raccoon
Shrews
   Vagrant shrew
Rodents
   Yellow-bellied marmot
   Townsend's ground
      squirrel
   Washington ground
      squirrel
   Least chipmunk
   Northern pocket gopher
   Great Basin pocket
      mouse
   Ord's kangaroo rat
   Beaver
   Deer mouse
   Northern grasshopper
      mouse
   Bushy-tailed wood rat
   Long-tailed vole
   Sagebrush vole
   Muskrat
   Porcupine
Rabbit and Hares
   White-tailed jackrabbit
      (rare)
   Black-tailed jackrabbit
      (rare)

   Mountain cottontail
Weasels, Mink and Otter
   Long-tailed weasel
   Striped skunk
   Badger
   American river otter
   Mink
Deer
   Elk (wapiti) (rare)
   Mule deer
Bovine
   Bighorn sheep (rare)

REPTILES

Painted turtle
Short-horned lizard
Sagebrush lizard
Western fence lizard
Side-blotched lizard
Western skink
Racer
Night snake
Striped whipsnake (rare)
Pacific gopher snake
Common garter snake
Western rattlesnake

AMPHIBIANS

Long-toed salamander
Tiger salamander
Woodhouse's toad
Pacific chorus frog
Great Basin spadefoot toad

BIRDS

*This bird list follows 1998 7th edition
of the American Ornithologists' Union
Check-list to the Birds of North
America with the 2003 supplement.*
Waterfowl
   Trumpeter swan
   Tundra swan
   Canada geese
   Greater white-fronted
      geese
   Ross's geese
   Snow geese
   Wood duck
   Mallard
   Gadwall
   Northern pintail
   American wigeon
   Eurasian wigeon
   Northern shoveler

Cinnamon teal
Blue-winged teal
Green-winged teal
Canvasback
Redhead
Ring-necked duck
Greater scaup
Lesser scaup
Steller's eider (once)
Surf scoter
White-winged scoter
Long-tailed duck
Common goldeneye
Barrow's goldeneye
Bufflehead
Hooded merganser
Common merganser
Ruddy duck

Upland Game Birds
    All native species
        extirpated from
        Wallula Gap
Loons and Grebes
    Common loon
    Pacific loon
    Pied-billed grebe
    Horned grebe
    Eared grebe
    Western grebe

Clark's grebe
Red-necked grebe

Pelicans, Herons, Ibis
    American white pelican
    Double-crested
        cormorant
    American bittern
    Great blue heron
    Great egret
    Snowy egret
    Cattle egret
    Black-crowned night-
        heron
    White-faced ibis
Vultures
    Turkey vulture
Diurnal Raptors
    Osprey
    Bald eagle
    Northern harrier
    Sharp-shinned hawk
    Cooper's hawk
    Northern goshawk
    Red-shouldered hawk
    Swainson's hawk
    Red-tailed hawk
    Ferruginous hawk
    Rough-legged hawk
    Golden eagle

American kestrel
Merlin
Peregrine falcon
Prairie falcon

Rails and Cranes
    Virginia rail
    Sora
    American coot
    Sandhill crane
Shorebirds
    Black-bellied plover
    American golden plover
    Snowy plover
    Semipalmated plover
    Killdeer
    Black-necked stilt
    American avocet
    Greater yellowlegs
    Lesser yellowlegs
    Solitary sandpiper
    Willet
    Whimbrel
    Spotted sandpiper
    Long-billed curlew
    Hudsonian godwit
    Marbled godwit
    Ruddy turnstone
    Red knot
    Sanderling

Semipalmated sandpiper
Western sandpiper
Least sandpiper
Baird's sandpiper
Pectoral sandpiper
Sharp-tailed sandpiper
Dunlin
Stilt sandpiper
Ruff
Short-billed dowitcher
Long-billed dowitcher
Wilson's snipe
Wilson's phalarope
Red-necked phalarope
Red phalarope

Jaegers, Gulls, Terns
    Parasitic jaeger
    Long-tailed jaeger
    Franklin's gull
    Bonaparte's gull
    Mew gull
    Ring-billed gull
    California gull
    Herring gull
    Thayer's gull
    Iceland gull
    Lesser black-backed gull
    Western gull
    Glaucous-winged gull

Glaucous gull
Sabine's gull
Black-legged kittiwake
Caspian tern
Common tern
Forster's tern
Black tern

Doves
Mourning dove
Owls
Barn owl
Western screech-owl
Great horned owl
Western burrowing owl
(rare)
Long-eared owl
Short-eared owl (rare)
Northern saw-whet owl
Nightjars and Swifts
Common nighthawk
Common poorwill
Vaux's swift
White-throated swift
Hummingbirds
Black-chinned
hummingbird
Rufous hummingbird
Kingfishers
Belted kingfisher

Woodpeckers
Lewis's woodpecker
Red-naped sapsucker
Downy woodpecker
Hairy woodpecker
Northern flicker
Flycatchers
Olive-sided flycatcher
Western wood-pewee
Western flycatcher
Willow flycatcher
Hammond's flycatcher
Gray flycatcher
Dusky flycatcher
Say's phoebe
Western kingbird
Eastern kingbird
Shrikes
Loggerhead shrike
Northern shrike
Vireos
Warbling vireo
Cassin's vireo
Corvids
Black-billed magpie
American crow
Common raven

Larks, Swallows
Horned lark
Tree swallow
Violet-green swallow
Northern rough-winged
swallow
Bank swallow
Cliff swallow
Barn swallow
Chickadees
Black-capped chickadee
Wrens
Rock wren
Canyon wren
House wren
Winter wren
Marsh wren
Kinglets
Ruby-crowned kinglet
Thrushes
Western bluebird
Mountain bluebird
Hermit thrush
American robin
Varied thrush
Mimids
Sage thrasher

Waxwings
Bohemian waxwing
Cedar waxwing
Warblers
Orange-crowned warbler
Nashville warbler
Yellow warbler
Yellow-rumped warbler
Townsend's warbler
Prairie warbler
American redstart
Northern waterthrush
MacGillivray's warbler
Common yellowthroat
(rare)
Wilson's warbler
Yellow-breasted chat
Tanagers
Western tanager
Sparrows
Spotted towhee
American tree sparrow
Chipping sparrow
Clay-colored sparrow
Brewer's sparrow
Vesper sparrow
Lark sparrow
Sage sparrow
Savannah sparrow

Fox sparrow
Song sparrow
Lincoln's sparrow
White-throated sparrow
Harris's sparrow
White-crowned sparrow
Golden-crowned
   sparrow
Dark-eyed junco
Black-headed grosbeak
Lazuli bunting

Blackbirds
   Red-winged blackbird
   Western meadowlark
   Yellow-headed blackbird
   Rusty blackbird
   Brewer's blackbird
   Common grackle
   Brown-headed cowbird
   Bullock's oriole
Finches
   Gray-crowned rosy finch
   Pine grosbeak
   Cassin's finch
   House finch
   Common redpoll
   Pine siskin
   American goldfinch
   Evening grosbeak

FISH
Pacific lamprey
White sturgeon
Mountain whitefish
Bull trout
Cutthroat trout
Rainbow trout
Steelhead
Chinook salmon
Coho salmon
Sockeye salmon
Chiselmouth
Northern pikeminnow
Redside shiner
Peamouth
Longnose dace
Largescale sucker

PLANTS

Trees
   Western juniper
   Netleaf hackberry
   Black cottonwood
   Water birch
   White alder
   Coyote willow
   Pacific willow
   Peach leaf willow

Woody Shrubs
   Basin sagebrush
   Big Wyoming sage
   Stiff sage
   Gray rabbitbrush
   Green rabbitbrush
   Common chokecherry
   Bitterbrush/antelope
      bush
   Golden currant
   Poison oak
   Hopsage
   Wormwood
   Winterfat
   Blue elderberry
Forbs
   Fiddleneck
   Puccoon
   Desert buckwheat
   Northern desert
      buckwheat
   Thyme desert buckwheat
   Common larkspur
   Sand dock
   Yellow prickly pear
      cactus
   Golden bee plant
   White-stemmed evening
      primrose

Yellow monkey-flower
Hot rock penstemon
Desert paintbrush
Wild flax
Orange globe mallow
Wild onion
Yellow bell
Blazing star
Thelypodium
Prairie rocket/wall
   flower
Salt and pepper
Gray's desert parsley
Woolly-pod locoweed
Hanging-pod locoweed
Showy phlox
Shooting star
Worm-leaf stonecrop
Plains daisy
Arrow-leaf balsamroot
Rosy balsamroot (re-
   discovered above the
   gap)
Mule's ears
Gold star
Utah Thistle
Yarrow
Yellow prairie violet

Native Grasses

    Bluebunch wheatgrass

    Steppe bluegrass

    Idaho fescue

    Needle and thread grass

    Indian rice grass

    Great Basin wild rye

    Sandberg's bunchgrass

    Creeping salt grass

The following is a list of **non-native, introduced species** found within the gap, in no particular order:

    Norwegian rat

    House mouse

    European starling

    Rock pigeon

    English sparrow

    Chukar

    Gray partridge

    California quail

    Wild turkey

    Ring-necked pheasant

    White-tailed deer

    Largemouth bass

    Smallmouth bass

    Walleye pike

    Yellow perch

    Black crappie

    White crappie

    Bluegill

    Shad

    Carp

    Asian clam

    Tumble mustard

    Cheatgrass

    Russian thistle

    Yellow starthistle

    Diffuse knapweed

    Leafy spurge

    Kochia

    Longspine sandbur

    Scotch thistle

    Purple loosestrife

    Russian olive

    Russian knapweed

    Spotted knapweed

    Rush skeletonweed

    China lettuce

    Puncture vine

    Dalmation toadflax

    Phragmities

    False indigo

    Reed canary grass

    Feral house cats

Coyote. (John Clement photo)

Mule deer. (Paul Clement photo)

Bighorn sheep. (John Clement photo)

Elk. (John Clement photo)

American river otter. (Paul Clement photo)

Western rattlesnake. (Mike Denny photo)

Long-toed salamander. (Mike Denny photo)

Bald eagle. (Bob Carson photo)

Western kingbird. (Paul Clement photo)

American white pelican. (Paul Clement photo)

Lazuli bunting. (Paul Clement photo)

Osprey. (Bob Carson photo)

Western meadowlark. (Paul Clement photo)

American avocet. (Paul Clement photo)

Cooper's hawk. (Paul Clement photo)

Yellow warbler. (Paul Clement photo)

Black-crowned night heron. (Paul Clement)

Barrow's goldeneye. (Bob Carson photo)

Sandhill cranes in flight. (Philip Fenner photo)

Western burrowing owl. (John Clement photo)

Green rabbitbrush in summer. (John Clement photo)

Phlox and rabbitbrush in spring. (John Clement photo)

Purple sage (*Salvia*) and basin sagebrush (*Artemisia*). (John Clement photo)

Rosy balsamroot, a rare plant, growing up through woolly-pod locoweed in spring bloom. (John Clement photo)

Fauna and Flora at Wallula Gap   207

Jacob's ladder. (John Clement photo)

Anise swallowtail on arrow-leaf balsam-root bloom. (John Clement photo)

Parry's daisy. (John Clement photo)

Wall flower. (Bob Carson photo)

Snow buckwheat, late fall. (Bob Carson)

Purple sage. (John Clement photo)

Gray rabbitbrush. (Bob Carson photo)

Woolly-pod locoweed. (Bob Carson photo)

Snow buckwheat, late summer. (Bob Carson)

White-stemmed evening primrose. (John Clement)

Green-banded mariposa lily. (Bob Carson)

Long-leaf phlox. (John Clement photo)

Prairie star. (John Clement photo)

Common larkspur. (Bob Carson photo)

USGS TOPOGRAPHIC MAPS (and date of publication)				
Scale	Northwest	Northeast	Southwest	Southeast
1:250,000 (1"= 4 miles)	Walla Walla (1953)		Pendleton (1953)	
1:125,000 (1" = 2 miles)	Pasco (1917)	Wallula (1918)	Umatilla (1908)	Pendleton (1936)
1:100,000 (1 cm = 1 km)	Richland (1978)	Walla Walla (1980)	Hermiston (1984)	Pendleton (1983)
1:24,000 (1" = 0.4 mile)	Nine Canyon (1964)	Wallula (1964)	Juniper (1962)	Juniper Canyon (1966)

Contributors' Biographies

Robert Baker was born in Stockton, California, and moved to Walla Walla, Washington in 1953. He has been interested in photography since receiving his first camera at the age of 10. For many years his photography consisted of the usual family pictures, but when he joined the newly formed Blue Mountain Photo Club in 1997, he began to take a more serious approach to picture making. Recently, Baker made the switch to digital and loves the added control of his images. His prints and/or cards are available at Fenton-Stahl Gallery, Holly's Flowers and other businesses in Walla Walla, and he has been featured in the *Union Bulletin*, *Foyer Magazine* and local brochures and websites. His biggest joy, however, is being featured in "galleries" in his relatives' homes in Carlsbad, California, and Bellingham and Walla Walla, Washington.

Robert J. Carson is Phillips Professor of Geology and Environmental Studies at Whitman College in Walla Walla, Washington. After he earned a Bachelor of Arts in geology from Cornell University, he worked for Texaco Inc. His other geology degrees are a Master of Science from Tulane University and a doctorate from the University of Washington. Summer employment included Washington's Department of Ecology and Division of Geology and Earth Resources. His interests are in the

earth and environmental sciences, and his courses deal with resources and pollution, human interaction with the biosphere, glaciers, volcanoes, water, landforms and natural hazards. A whitewater guide and a member of the American Alpine Club, he has led field trips in Africa, Eurasia, South America and throughout North America. Through the years, he developed a love for Wallula Gap. To complete this book on this National Natural Landmark, he enlisted several colleagues and photographers. His other books include *Hiking Guide to Washington Geology* and *East of Yellowstone: Geology of Clarks Fork Valley and the Nearby Beartooth and Absaroka Mountains*, published by Keokee Books in 2009 and 2010, respectively.

John Clement lives in Kennewick, Washington, and began his career in photography in the mid-1970s. He earned a Master of Photography degree from Professional Photographers of America. He has received more than 55 regional, national and international awards for pictorial and commercial photography. Providing the photography, Clement has co-published the books *Palouse Country: A Land and its People* and *The Wenatchee Valley and its First People* with writer Richard Scheuerman. The two also collaborated on the book *Finding Chief Kamiakin*, published by Washington State University in 2008. His latest projects are the 2011 Northwest Drylands calendar and a companion book titled *Northwest Drylands: Illuminated Earth-Sky Connections*, a biography about the photographer by Scheuerman. A sampling of Clement's work can be viewed at www.johnclementgallery.com.

Paul Clement is a flight test engineer for an aerospace company in Seattle as well as an amateur photographer. Clement was born in 1948 and grew up in Richland, Washington, where he developed an interest in photography as well as wildlife – caring for dozens of wild birds and animals as well as taking photographs and doing his own developing and printing. Recently he acquired all-digital equipment and has been pursuing animals in the wild with a focus on action photography. Most of Clement's current photography documents flora and fauna from eastern Washington. This book is his first published photography.

Michael E. Denny was born in Klamath Falls, Oregon, but spent part of his childhood in southeast Africa where he developed an appreciation for the natural world. He later attended high school in Burns, Oregon, and Caldwell, Idaho, and studied biology and art at Walla Walla College. Denny has worked as a private wildlife contractor, in bird and small vertebrate work for the U.S. Forest Service, and on vegetative surveys. He has written articles on Northwest birds in regional journals and contributed to books on birds of Oregon and Washington. He illustrated *A Birder's Guide to Idaho* and co-authored *Birds of the Inland Northwest and Northern Rockies* and *The Birds of Interior BC and the Rockies*. He currently works as the riparian habitat coordinator for the Walla Walla County Conservation District and sits on the boards of the Blue Mountain Audubon Society and the Tri-State Steelheaders. He is a member of the Washington Ornithological Society, Oregon Field

Ornithologists and Northwest Vertebrate Biologists. He speaks and leads wildlife tours for many organizations and festivals in an effort to educate others about the outstanding value of the life-sustaining natural world. He and his wife, MerryLynn, live in College Place, Washington.

Catherine E. Dickson began working as an archaeologist in 1990 when she realized she could be paid for walking around in the woods all day finding amazing things. She received her Bachelor of Arts in anthropology from Pomona College in 1992 and Master of Arts in anthropology from Oregon State University in 1997. Her master's program concentrated on cultural resource management and historic sites archaeology. Her thesis considered public participation in archaeology. Dickson lives in La Grande, Oregon where she works as an archaeologist and farmer with her partner, Shawn, cat Shakespeare, and dog Andy.

Lawrence L. Dodd is a native of the Walla Walla Valley and a member of a family that settled in the valley in 1869. A 1957 graduate of Washington State College, he then served four and a half years in the U.S. Air Force before returning to the family farm. He worked at Whitman Mission National Historic Site before starting a 34-year career at Whitman College, retiring in 2003 as the first Whitman College archivist. In retirement Dodd continues his research in local and family history and spending time improving the family farm.

G. Thomas Edwards earned a Bachelor of Arts in history from Willamette University and a Master of Arts and a doctorate in history from the University of Oregon. He taught for 34 years at Whitman College but also taught at several universities, including Southern University in Baton Rouge. He wrote *Sowing Good Seeds: The Northwest Suffrage Campaigns of Susan B. Anthony*, a two-volume history of Whitman College, and co-edited *Experiences in a Promised Land*. He published essays on Civil War, Western and Pacific Northwest subjects. He and his wife now reside in Portland, Oregon.

Kathryn Farrell Guizar migrated in 1990 from the Detroit area to attend Whitman College, where she majored in studio art. Love for the high desert plains of the "east side" has kept her here in Walla Walla. She, along with her two daughters Kara and Allie, enjoy rural living on their acre "farm" with a micro vineyard, three cats, two dogs, and 15 chickens. Time after a regular job is spent divided between the girls' 4-H activities, the Walla Walla Valley Farmers Market, grant writing for pedestrian issues, swimming, and photography for fun and profit with her home-based business Image Management.

Dianne Kornberg was trained as a painter, but her medium for 25 years has been photography. In her work she represents the aesthetics and metaphorical ideas she finds in the natural world. Raised in Richland, Washington, she received her Bachelor of Fine Arts from the University of Washington and her Master of Fine Arts from Indiana

University. She is a Professor Emerita at Pacific Northwest College of Art in Portland, Oregon, and works and resides in the San Juan Islands in Washington. Kornberg has exhibited her work throughout the United States and internationally in more than 20 solo exhibitions. Her work is represented in several important museum collections and has been featured in book publications including *Contemporary Art in the Northwest*, *100 Artists of the West Coast*, and *Selected Works of the Portland Art Museum*. Two monographs of her work have been published: *Field Notes, Photographs by Dianne Kornberg, 1992-2007* and *India Tigers*.

Donald Snow is a professor, editor, writer and activist with more than 30 years of experience in environmental issues. For 18 of those years he directed the Northern Lights Research & Education Institute in Missoula, Montana, where he founded and co-edited both *Northern Lights Magazine* and the *Chronicle of Community*. In 2001 he took up residence in Walla Walla, Washington, and began teaching at Whitman College where he is now senior lecturer of environmental humanities. His essays and stories have appeared in *Orion*, *Sierra*, *Gray's Sporting Journal*, *Montana Magazine*, *High Country News* and many other periodicals. In 2006, the Oregon Council for the Humanities published his lecture, "Round the Next Bend: Pendleton, Walla Walla, and the Transformation of the Rural West." His books as editor and contributor include *The Book of the Tongass*, *The Next West* and *Northern Lights: A Selection of New Writing from the American West*.

Index

An italicized page number indicates a photo, illustration or table.